"*The powerful techniques taught by Pam Gross and Pete Paskill gave me the confidence and skills to get the job that fits me to a "T." These techniques have been invaluable to me. Anyone looking for a job or contemplating a career change can apply these same methods to take control of his or her own future.*"

Jim Strain
Senior Human Resources Rep

"*As a result of the tools presented in this book, we both are doing something we enjoy and find satisfying. This material allowed us to take control of our careers and get what we wanted from our work. It changed our lives.*"

Andy and Julie Job

## DEDICATION

This book is dedicated to Dr. James C.
Petersen and his congregation at
Southminster Presbyterian Church in
Beaverton, Oregon, without whose time,
energy, talent and money CareerMakers
would not have come into being in 1983.

## ACKNOWLEDGEMENTS

A healthy partnership is a wonderful thing. It allows people to grow, change and express their uniqueness under the umbrella of grace. This book comes out of such a partnership.

Pete and I have been partners at CareerMakers since mid-1984. Together we have established a dynamic life planning/job search course of study. And, we have helped over 2,000 people through job or career transition. The program is successful because of the partnership and the commitment that each of us brings to it.

When we made the commitment to write the book, Pete agreed to manage CareerMakers single-handedly while I put the words on paper. The words express our accumulated thoughts on the job-search process. And so, I claim authorship with the clear understanding that there would be no book without the unconditional support of my partner.

Our spouses deserve cheers and a standing ovation. Ron Gross willingly read every word of every revision, and was an attentive listener to much teeth-gnashing. Jana Paskill willingly propped up a sagging, over-committed, sometimes exhausted husband. We not only survived the project, we are still friends.

The publishing process was managed by Sally Petersen who swooped in with timetables, delegated tasks and communicated encouragement. She kept us moving toward and through various deadlines with a delicate balance of rigidity, grace and aplomb rarely found outside convents. And, we are still friends.

Our thanks to Lisa Petersen who read and edited all the words, words, words!!

And, there are those people whose words and deeds kept us going. Those folks include Gayle Rathbun, Vicki Price, Denny Buell, Suzy Edwards, Dottie and Clayton Davidson, Jan Marshall, Becky Corcoran, Bill Whitlock, Anne Hudson, Bill Norman, Geraldine Bell, Gene Kugler, Marie Morgan, Anne Rystrom, Hugh Moore, Dick Bittinger, Peter Jackson, Al Peterman and Georgia and Howard Walp. We can't omit our U.S. Bank bunch — Chuck Long, Curt Meyers and Sherre Barnett.

CareerMakers, a non-profit organization, received funding from the Meyer Memorial Trust, Oregon Community Foundation, Murdock Charitable Trust, Templeton Foundation and Southminster Presbyterian Church. In addition, in-kind donations have come from U.S. Bank, Nike and Nerco. This generosity has been critical to our success.

How about the wonderful 2,000? Without all those Career-Makers' graduates, there would be no Ten Truths, no BRIDGE method, no Gracious Art of Networking. This book is truly about them and their experiences with their personal career explorations and job searches. We have learned so much about the process through their successes and defeats, joys and heartaches that it would be criminal to not share it with others.

Specific graduates need to be acknowledged. These are the ones who graciously allowed their stories to be told in the "Cases in Point" found in Chapter I: The Ten Truths. They are Ken McCormick, Shirley Quinn, Julie Job, Ron Gross, Michael Schroeder, Donna Acord, Connie Hahs, Gene Nudelman, Kate Nelson, Anne Hudson, Dave Wilson, Will Werner and Homer Speer.

*Pam Gross*

# WANT A
## NEW
## BETTER
## FANTASTIC
# JOB?

*A How-To Manual for the Serious Job Seeker*

by
Pam Gross • Peter Paskill

Published by
RightSide Resources, Lake Oswego, OR, USA

Cover design: Ruth Brandt-Miller, Ron Bohart

Reprinted 1993
Reprinted 1994
Reprinted 1995

ISBN: 0-9630012-0-5

Printed in the United States of America

CareerMakers, Inc.
1336 SW Bertha Blvd.
Portland, Oregon   97219
(503) 244-1055

# Contents

# INTRODUCTION

The name of our game is street-wise practicality. We know what works and what doesn't when it comes to issues of job search and career transition.

That is why this book is all about "doing it."

It is about how to do a job search and make a career change. It contains a tested, tried and true method of changing jobs or careers that has worked for hundreds of people. We developed this BRIDGE method at CareerMakers in Portland, Oregon. It has been used by over 2,000 people, most of whom landed new, better, fantastic jobs.

Chapter I: **Ten Truths** is your reality check. It addresses mistakes most job seekers make as they pursue their next job or career. As you read the Truths, you may discover why your job search activities have not produced the results you hoped for. You will gain insights into how to think and behave differently so you can conduct a more efficient job search.

Chapter II: **The New Way Job Search** illustrates the BRIDGE method of job search or career change. You will learn the skills required to effect job or career change graciously and effectively, including the seven rules for researching the job market. You will learn how to organize yourself for your job search or career exploration. Also, you will learn how to write proposals to create jobs for yourself. *If you are thinking about consulting or going into your own business, the BRIDGE method will provide information that is invaluable to your success.*

Chapter III: **Homework** provides a series of exercises. They will not take forever to complete and the results will please you. When you're finished, you'll know what you need in a job so you will be happy as you go to work on Monday mornings.

If you are serious about getting on with your job search, or thinking about changing careers, you would do well to take advantage of the experiences of those 2,000 who have gone before you. They don't say, "Thank God it's Friday" any more, and they are no longer intimidated by the thought of changing careers or finding a new job, because they know how to "do it."

Chapter I

# THE TEN TRUTHS
# OF JOB OR CAREER TRANSITION

## TRUTH #1

**In most cases people hire people they know and like — whether or not the candidate has the exact experience, background or skills to do the job.**

First of all, most hiring managers have little interest in hiring. They just don't want to take the time to screen candidates, interview and then select. Words we frequently hear them say are, "I can't stand the thought of running an ad in the paper." All they want is the position filled so that they can get on with their managing. And so, when faced with the hiring nightmare, these managers are likely to say to everyone they see, "I need to hire somebody. Do you know anyone?"

Secondly, managers are fearful. They do not want to make a mistake and hire the wrong person. If that happens, they look bad in the eyes of their boss, and all the stuff that needs to be done won't get done. Then they will have the problems they have now *plus* they will have to get rid of the new hire and go through the hiring process all over again.

This is why so many positions are filled from within an organization or by an outsider with inside connections. In fact, the truth is that the manager's neighbor's cousin whom he has never met is a more viable candidate for an opening than one who sends in a resume. People want to hire a known quantity — even a little known quantity — over a total stranger.

If you spend all of your time doing an old way job search, you respond to newspaper ads by sending out resumes. This means you fall into the "stranger" category. Your phone does not ring with invitations to interview — and you are probably pretty frustrated and upset.

### CASE IN POINT:

Ken, 23, came to CareerMakers because he was discouraged with the job search. He made a nice appearance, held a degree with a more-than-respectable grade point average and was well-rounded with interests in jazz trombone and skiing.

In class Ken determined he was interested in sales and marketing. He arranged an information interview with a classmate's wife who worked in advertising sales at a television station.

Ken followed up and learned much about television ad sales. As he was leaving, the woman asked if he had any interest in production. He pleaded ignorance and she explained that television production involved the technical nuts and bolts of putting shows together — lights, camera, sets, make-up. "Sure," he said. "I'd like to know about that."

She introduced Ken to the executive producer of a well-known nightly program who talked with him about production. Thirty minutes later, the producer said, "If you are really interested in this, I have an opening for a beginning production person. Would you like to pursue it?"

"Well, yes," our student said.

"O.K. I need a resume Monday morning."

"Well, what would I put on it? I have no real-life experience that relates to this."

"Illustrate a couple of your college projects. That will be enough."

And Ken wrote a resume which illustrated two college projects that had to do with market research. He hand-carried his resume to the station on Monday morning, interviewed and got the job as floor director *even though he barely knew a lens cap from a tripod.*

Why?

Because he was a known quantity (albeit little known) to the person who had the power to hire him. The manager chose him over all the other applicants (strangers), many with communication degrees and the applicable technical skills.

CASE IN POINT:

Shirley, 48, had been a registered nurse for about twenty-five years. She was tired of nursing but did not know what she wanted to do next. She embarked on a job search in January and when her daughter's boyfriend learned she had extra time, he asked Shirley to consider helping out at his C.P.A. firm. "Sure," she said. "Why not?"

Knowing little about the business world, let alone accounting, Shirley began working fifteen hours a week at minimum wage. Much to her surprise, she found the work interesting and challenging. The pace picked up as the calendar rolled into April 15, and she found herself caught up in a race to the finish. When tax season ended, the firm's owner asked her to stay. She accepted.

Today, Shirley manages the firm's 18-member office staff.

Shirley became a known quantity to the owner of the firm. He got to know her as someone who could make a contribution to the company. Therefore, her nursing background was not an obstacle in her career change.

**SUMMARY:**
Once you understand that people do not want to hire strangers, it becomes your task to make a lot of new friends and notify the old ones that you are looking for work. Doing this in a structured and directed manner is called networking.

**TRUTH #2**
**Most jobs that are available this minute are not advertised or posted anywhere. These unadvertised jobs constitute the "hidden job market."**

Once upon a time a career counselor came up with the phrase "hidden job market" and assigned a percentage to it. Forever more, career counselors have reeled off the phrase and its percentage as a sacred litany. "You know, 85 per cent of jobs available right now are not advertised," they say to bewildered job seekers. "You must tap into the hidden job market."

This usually scares job seekers for several reasons. First, imaginations run wild with visions of this hidden job market as some cave deep within the bowels of the planet with enormous iron gates at its entrance, locked with the mightiest of padlocks to which only career counselors have the key. Of course, behind the gates one is to find all those unadvertised jobs.

Second, logic takes over (always a terrible detriment to job seekers). "Yeah," logic says, "Well, if these jobs are unadvertised, how am I supposed to find them? The ones I know about are, logically, advertised in the paper."

And finally, even if job seekers believe the notion of a hidden job market, they won't swallow the bit about the 85 per cent. We at CareerMakers know of no statistics that support that percentage, but our best estimate is that more than 65 per cent of our graduates wind up in jobs that weren't advertised.

So, what is this hidden job market?

No cave. No iron gate. No mighty padlock.

The hidden job market is, simply, unadvertised jobs that are found through people. The more people you know, and the more people who know you're looking for work, the more you increase your chances of finding or creating a job. Since managers don't want to spend time with the hiring process, they are likely to ask their peers to suggest anyone who might fit the job description. If one of their peers is someone you know, you may have a job lead.

This is the way most jobs are filled.

CASE IN POINT:
Julie, 30, decided that she wanted to start her own business of organizing things, primarily people's offices. Her target market is people who can't keep track of stuff that they know they should keep track of. She began her business by bartering time and skills to get some "real-life"

experience and references. She also kept in touch with us at CareerMakers. We knew not only exactly what she wanted to do but that she was, indeed, doing it.

Then one Monday morning we received a letter from a woman who had begun working at home on a book. She needed someone to help her organize her home office and to keep her organized. In fact, she described herself as "terminally disorganized."

We called Julie and connected her with her first disorganized client. She was hired by 2:00 the same day.

CASE IN POINT:

Ron, 52, decided to liquidate his woodworking business after the recession of the early '80s had done it in, but he wanted to remain in the industry. So he targeted three companies he would like to work for, based on his knowledge of the company owners. He had come to know the owners during years of involvement with the Cabinetmakers' Apprenticeship Board.

Ron invited the first company owner to lunch. They talked about Ron's former business. They talked about the company and its needs. They talked about the skills required to fill those needs. They talked about Ron's skills as they related to those needs.

After another meeting and a tour of the business, Ron was hired, *even though the company did not have a specific opening.*

SUMMARY:

This is how the hidden job market works. People get jobs through other people — people who know them and know what they are looking for. That is when referrals take place and new jobs are created.

## TRUTH #3

**There is a structured and directed manner of accessing the hidden job market. It is a networking process called the New Way job search, and most people don't know how to do it effectively.**

The most frequent comment we at CareerMakers hear about networking is that it doesn't work. The reason it doesn't work is that people do it wrong.

Your next job will most likely come to you through another person rather than an ad in the paper. We know that people hire people they know and like. So, it makes sense to develop relationships with as many people as possible. Job seekers who have a well-developed network *before* they must do a job search find work more quickly than those starting from scratch. The point is networking is not just about getting a job—networking is a way of life.

The New Way job search is a three-stage networking process. It is necessary to carry out all three stages of activity conducting a job search. They are:

> 1. Busybodying
> 2. Researching
> 3. Generating job interviews

(Chapter II tells precisely how to do a New Way job search.)

### BUSYBODYING
Since you do not know which person will put you on the path to a job, talk to anyone, anytime, anywhere. This is

called Busybodying, and it means striking up conversations in grocery store lines, at church or temple coffee hour, in classes, at association meetings or with neighbors. This is also known as schmoozing.

### RESEARCHING

Here is where most people fail in their job search. They do not do their research. Plainly and simply, it means doing information interviews to make solid decisions about what you want to do and where you want to do it.

Identify three things (industries, companies or job titles) that interest you and begin calling people in those areas of interest. Talk to them about what they do, how they do it, and what challenges they are facing. Talk to at least eight people in each interest area just to learn what's "out there." *This is the only valid way to learn about the job market.*

By researching, you learn the reality of the job market. You validate or invalidate assumptions you have about yourself and your interests, and you erase question marks about industries, companies and job titles. You meet people who come to like you, who, in the future, may recommend you for jobs. You make solid decisions about what you want to do. Most importantly, you will meet people who share your interests and are willing to help with your job search.

Set up a networking notebook to keep track of the people you interview. Take notes on what you learn. Use the information to make career decisions. Keep a calendar so you know who you're seeing when. Buy business cards that say your name, address and phone number *only.* Think of them as confetti and sprinkle them all over town. Write a thank-you note to everyone who is gracious enough to see you — and enclose a confetti card.

Those who do not, for whatever reasons, do the research stage of networking take longest to find a job. They also feel most depressed, angry and hopeless in their job search.

And, those who do not organize themselves in their job search lose credibility with the very people they are trying to impress.

### GENERATING JOB INTERVIEWS

After you have narrowed down what job or career you want to pursue, you begin generating job interviews. There are three basic ways to do this: getting referrals from people, writing proposals to create a job, and answering newspaper ads. Overwhelmingly, most people get job interviews through referrals.

This, in a nutshell, is how to do a New Way job search. The result is finding an enjoyable and satisfying job.

### SUMMARY:

Learn how to do a New Way job search. Become a skilled networker. Not only will you find a job you like, you will learn skills that are critical to your very survival in our ever-changing, complex world.

### TRUTH #4

**Until you take yourself seriously and come to grips with your skills, values and interests — the essence of who you are — you will not find enjoyable and satisfying work.**

You may think you know who you are, and, when asked, you can talk about your job titles or degrees. But you are much, much more than job titles and degrees. Unless you have taken self-exploration time in a life-planning class, you probably are not in touch with your skills, values and interests.

An assessment of skills, values and interests (done with real people, not a computer), puts you in touch with your uniqueness. Then you must take your uniqueness seriously and search for work that not only lets you express it but pays you for doing so.

A New Way job search is interest-driven. By following your true interests, you can approach the otherwise arduous task of networking/researching with curiosity and enthusiasm. This energy fosters a positive attitude about yourself and the job search and gives you inner strength. You will take yourself seriously and be taken seriously by others. Without this energy, finding or creating a new, better, fantastic job will be difficult, if not impossible.


CASE IN POINT:
After college, Michael, 28, used a biology degree to land a job as a technician in a hospital pharmacy. Two years later he was sick of his job. It was boring, unchallenging and he felt restless. At CareerMakers he discovered that his true love was putting events and shows together. But his degree had no bearing on this passion. In fact, aside from planning events in college, he had no "professional" experience.

Michael started a New Way job search by talking with nearly fifty professional event planners. Once he knew what it was about and the people involved, he targeted several top companies and began to generate job interviews within them. He landed a plum job with an organization that plans big trade shows and, today, he gets paid for setting up state-of-the-art displays.

Now, Michael is challenged each day, engaged with the activities of the job, and he smiles a lot.

### CASE IN POINT:

Donna, a woman in her mid-thirties with an engineering degree and an MBA from Stanford, became bone-tired of putting together marketing plans for high-tech products. When her company downsized, she volunteered to go. When she got in touch with her values and interests, she realized that she really wanted to help at-risk youth. But her chances, she felt, were slim to none with her background.

Donna began researching. She talked with people in public schools — teachers, administrators, special-projects staff. Then she went to the state level. She made friends with these people. They liked her fresh approach. They liked her business background. They thought she would be wonderful working as a business liaison for the public school system. She could form business-education partnerships to benefit at-risk youth. She was hired.

Now, Donna feels she is making a difference.

### CASE IN POINT:

Connie, a mother of two young children, left a teaching job to spend more time with her children. But her job as a full-time mom was not as fulfilling as she thought it would be. Connie decided to take herself seriously and came to CareerMakers. While in class, she affirmed a strong interest in women's issues and validated her skills in advocacy. She became quite clear that she wanted a part-time job at this stage in her life.

Connie researched organizations that dealt with women's issues, uncovered several openings and targeted a part-time position as assistant to the director of a women's shelter. She was hired.

Now, Connie feels that her life is balanced. She is available for her children and she is stimulated by her job.

### CASE IN POINT:

Gene, 50, came to us after he had been out of work for a year. His family had decided to sell the family retail business he had been managing for years. Since he was well connected, he figured people would come to him with job possibilities. He got a lot of work done around the house that year. Then one day a friend asked how many business acquaintances had called with offers. "Now that you mention it," he said, "none." The friend urged him to go to CareerMakers.

While in class Gene found he enjoyed older people. He really liked being around them. He took his elderly parents on vacations and liked their elderly friends. So, he volunteered to help elderly people with home repairs and thoroughly enjoyed it. Then he talked with people in organizations that provided services for the elderly. One organization asked him to work at a low wage as a part-time fund director, and he agreed. He worked at that job for about six months. Then some grants came through and he got a full-time job at normal pay.

Now, Gene feels peaceful inside and more fulfilled.

### SUMMARY:

It is essential to take yourself seriously in a job search. If you don't, no one else will. If you want to smile a lot, make a difference, put your life in balance, feel peaceful inside, you must open yourself up to yourself— look inside and find what's in there that excites you. Those interests and passions are there — they are simply covered with dust, asleep, buried in cultural "shoulds" and "yes, buts."

Dust them off, wake them up, throw logic aside! Select three areas of interest and begin a New Way job search!

## TRUTH #5
**What "they" want is not nearly as important as what you want.**

Employers come in all shapes and sizes, and so do their wants. A common question from job seekers is, "What do they want, anyhow?" Simply put, it's not that simple.

Some employers want employees who can do everything. They want employees who can read their minds, make them lots of money, be creative, and cheerful at all times. In other words, "they" want employees who walk — no, skip — on water. Just read some of the job descriptions in the want ads.

Other employers don't honestly know what they want in an employee. They are not sure about the nature of the available job. Or, skills needed to do the job. Or, the interview process in general. They just want someone to do the job, period. The hiring process is a confusing detour from their day-to-day business. "They" want to get through it as quickly and as painlessly as possible, without hiring the wrong person.

Still others know with check-list accuracy the exact skills, traits and values they must hire to do the job.

As a job seeker, you will no doubt interview with all three types. That is why it's so important for you to assess your skills, values and interests so you know what you want in a job. During an interview, you should be able to say what you need to be productive and feel fulfilled. If you articulate your skills and values well and you don't get the job, it's just as well. The job was simply not a fit for your uniqueness.

By far, the most dynamic interviews take place between employers and candidates who both know what they want. Then a high level of information-sharing occurs. This spawns a great deal of enthusiasm and, usually, a job offer. If you accept such a job, you do so for all the right reasons.

Such dynamic interviews occur when a job seeker has done an appropriate amount of Researching. They rarely result from a cold resume sent in response to a want ad. In this situation, the job seeker has too many question marks about the company and job whizzing around in the brain. Still, if you know what you want and generate opportunities to interview blind, you may be able to clarify whether the job opening is one to pursue.

CASE IN POINT:

Kate, 45, was a terrific supervisor and organizer, and she loved cooking and teenagers. Most of her group cooking, however, had been done for church or camp. She had no formal training or professional experience in the cooking trade. As for teenagers, she had two of her own, but she had neither a teaching nor a counseling degree.

Kate began researching job possibilities and uncovered an opportunity to manage a restaurant that employed mostly teenagers. When she went for the interview, she knew exactly what she wanted: that job. She knew why: it fit her skills, interests and values perfectly. And, she had already met the boss when she did her Researching.

Kate and the boss had a wonderful time during the interview. He knew what he wanted. Because of her Researching, she knew what he wanted. Further, she knew she had what he wanted, and she conveyed her skills, values and interests with such conviction and enthusiasm that he hired her.

## CASE IN POINT:

When it was time to add staff at CareerMakers, we were pretty sure we wanted to hire Anne, a contract instructor teaching our night classes. We knew her. We liked her. She was enthusiastic, committed to the organization, and very competent. We figured she must like teaching for us because she kept on doing it.

Meanwhile, Anne had observed that classes were getting larger and things were hectic. Being a skilled networker, she asked me to lunch. At lunch she asked about the state of CareerMakers and our future needs. I allowed that we were thinking of adding staff and suggested she write a proposal.

Knowing our needs (right from the mare's mouth), Anne wrote a simple, humorous, one-page proposal stating what she wanted to do at CareerMakers. When she finished the proposal, she called me to set a time to discuss it. *She scheduled her own job interview.* Her wants were right on target with our needs. Surprised? Of course not. She had done her research thoroughly. The proposal was invaluable in clarifying both our wants and needs. The interview itself was just, well, supremely comfortable. The job was offered, and she accepted.

SUMMARY:

Do skills, values and interest assessment to determine what you want in a job. Do Stage II networking to research where you are likely to find it. When you interview, operate from the base of what you want. Find out if it's a fit with what "they" want. If so, great! If not, you don't want the job.

## TRUTH #6

**Tell me how you will make me money, save me money or save me time, and I will seriously consider you as a candidate for a position in my company, whether or not I have an opening.**

People who have the power to hire are always looking for dynamic people. If not, they are complacent managers, and you do not want to work for them. Why work for a person who will not listen to new ideas?

When you do your Researching to discover what is out there you should always ask, "What challenges are facing you in the next year?" Listen carefully to the answer because you could learn what you need to know to write a proposal and create a job.

You see, challenges translate to problems. Problems need to be solved. Your skills solve problems. The question you ask yourself is, "Do my skills solve these problems?" If the answer is "yes," you have what it takes to write a proposal. Realistically, it might take several information interviews to clarify problems. But, it is this "inside information" that allows you to know how your skills and values can enhance the company's bottom line.

CASE IN POINT:

Dave, 35, had been talking with the owners of a firm

that manufactured machines capable of making certain materials recyclable. The two owners had invented and designed the machines. Dave was very enthusiastic about the products and the company, and when he asked about challenges, the owners said they wanted to market the machines across the nation, but they did not know how that was done.

Dave knew how. He asked, "What do you want your sales to be in three years?" They told him. That was all the information he needed. Dave's proposal showed how, through sound marketing procedures, he would produce the desired amount in three years.

Dave was hired. There hadn't been a stated opening at that company. *The job did not exist until he defined it.*

### CASE IN POINT:

Will, 38, had worked nearly 12 years for the state in land acquisition. He was ready to move on but wasn't sure where he was going. Then things began to change. Private industry was beginning to get into land acquisition. Will saw a way to move his skills and knowledge into the private sector. He began to research companies that were most likely to get into the land acquisition business and found an interesting one.

Will asked how they planned to make the move. They said this, they said that, and they said other things. But it was clear they did not know how to get into land acquisition. So Will wrote a proposal that showed steps he would take to bring the company into the new, profitable market. His cover letter stated, "I am the person to create, launch and manage your land acquisition unit."

Will was hired. The second day on the job he called us

at CareerMakers and said, "I was just asked to give myself a title. They've never had one of me before."

**SUMMARY:**
Finding a job opening and filling it is one way to get a job. Creating a brand new job by writing a proposal showing how you can contribute to the bottom line is another way. It's awfully difficult to say no to a well-thought-out proposal.

## TRUTH #7
**The Prime Rule of the job search is: Open your mouth and talk to people — anyone, anywhere, anytime.**

If you are searching for a job, you may be experiencing some embarrassment at being unemployed. You may feel like there's something wrong with you. Your family seems focused on two questions: Why you lost your job — the *real* reason, and whether you have a new job yet. This suspicion is guilt producing, and it is tempting to clam up and avoid talking about the job search. Who wants to be interrogated all the time, anyway?

Now, let's assume these people mean well. If that's the case, they should be helping, not hindering, your efforts to find a job.

But, before you shove your significant other's nose into the last paragraph yelling, "See! You should be helping, for heaven's sake!" let us say *it is your responsibility to ask people to help you, and to tell them how they can help.* You see, they simply don't know how to help.

Start telling friends and acquaintances that you are in a job search. Stand up in church or temple if there is a "sharing time" and announce that you are in a job search. Ask for prayers — and *people to talk to for Researching.* Say to everyone you know, "I am currently researching human resources management and would like to talk with people in the field. Do you know anyone who's involved in human resources?"

## YOU CANNOT KEEP QUIET AND EXPECT TO DO A JOB SEARCH!!

Busybodying is a wonderful method of getting used to talking with all kinds of people and, possibly, uncovering job leads. Busybodying means talking to strangers in supermarkets, at your health club, in your neighborhood, anywhere. We call these interviews "friendly assaults," and, until you make them part of your life, you will not understand their value. Always remember: You do not know where your job will come from, but it will come through another person. Who? You don't know. Might be that guy waiting, as you are, to have tires put on the car. *Don't just sit there — talk to him!*

At CareerMakers, people get assignments to Busybody and then report on the outcome of the "friendly assaults." Sixty percent of the time, nothing much happens beyond a pleasant exchange with another human being (not bad either). People have engaging conversations with someone they would like to meet again about 20 percent of the time. Fifteen percent of the time a person comes away with the name of a person to call for an information interview. A job lead comes up 5 percent of the time.

CASE IN POINT:

One day at CareerMakers, Ron, 26, was assigned to Busybody. But, not giving this job search method any credibility, he tried to get it over with as soon as possible.

He went from class directly to a Quick-Mart to buy a soft drink and "assault" the first person he saw.

Ron observed a man enter the store, head straight for the soft-drink section and pick up three six packs of soda pop.

"Boy!" he said to the man, "You're really thirsty, aren't you?"

The man stopped short and assimilated the question. "Yes. But these aren't all for me. I'm working across the street and came over to get the stuff for our afternoon break."

"Oh. And what are you doing across the street?"

"Well, we have a huge inventory of car parts that we're putting on a computer system."

"That's interesting. What software are you using?"

"I don't know. That's not what I'm working on. But . . ." the man shifted the three six packs under one arm, reached into a pocket and handed Ron a business card, "George is looking for people to help with the computer part. You might want to give him a call."

Bingo!! A five percenter!!

Ron followed up. Although the job didn't fit him, the experience taught him the value of Busybodying.

**SUMMARY:**

You do not have the faintest idea who will put you on the path to a job. You must, to find or create your next job, tell people you are in a career exploration and ask who they might connect you with. Don't be embarrassed by your unemployment. Being unemployed presents you with an opportunity to find a wonderful new job, which could be better than the last one.

## TRUTH #8

### You do not need a resume to do a job search.

Who said the first thing you do to find a job is write a resume? Who said that a bright, savvy human being can encapsulate a lifetime of accomplishments within the confines of one 8 x 11" piece of paper? Who said resumes get people jobs?

Old way job search says you have to have a resume to play the game. New Way job search says you put a resume together if and when you need to, and then target it to the position you want. No more spending $300 on 150 resumes that will not get you a job.

Here's one exception. If you want to continue in the same field, a resume may work with the want ads. We call this a "cookie-cutter" situation. If you are an accountant, computer programmer or mechanical engineer, and your resume shows a chronologically progressive responsibility curve, you *might* get called in for an interview. Sending resumes to want ads works best with support positions, such as administrative assistants, secretaries, data entry workers and receptionists. This probably is because of constant demand for support personnel.

A New Way job search with a lot of Stage II networking, or Researching, does not require a resume. If you are looking into completely new areas of interest, how can you provide a resume? You simply can not know what to put on it until you've done your information interviews to find out what skills and knowledge are needed to get into that new field.

Once you are in Stage III networking, or Generating Job Interviews, you may or may not need a resume. Whether you need one depends upon how well you know the people doing the hiring. If you know them well, they may not even think about a resume.

Whenever someone requests a resume for a job opening, ask what should be highlighted. Ask what specific skills and traits are needed for the position. Ask what format they prefer -- and then give it to them. People have very strong views about what a resume *should be!* Try not to waste time putting together what you view as the perfect resume only to have it met with disdain by the person who has the power to hire you. In this case, give them what they want.

The resume book we recommend at CareerMakers is *The Damn Good Resume Book* by Yana Parker. It illustrates several different types of resume formats.

### CASE IN POINT:

Margie, 50, came to CareerMakers to prepare herself to re-enter the job market. She was in the middle of a divorce, and she hadn't worked in years. Her self-esteem was low, but she had not lost her sense of humor.

Three days after she finished class, Margie received a call from a friend about an opening for an office manager at a property management company. She had experience with personal rental properties and office management and her friend asked if she would like to interview for the position.

"Sure!" Margie said. Her friend set up an interview for 10 a.m. the next day and told Margie to bring a resume.

*Welllllll* — it was crisis time. Margie had a resume. Trouble was it had been typed on a 1955 portable type-writer. You know the kind—the letter *"a"* always splotched and the *"s"* dropped below the line of print. In other words, something typed perfectly looked terrible.

She called CareerMakers in a panic.
"What should I do? It's 5 p.m. and I'm supposed to be there at 10 in the morning with a resume! You know what my resume looks like!"

We suggested two alternatives. She could make herself a wreck at the interview by staying up all night preparing a resume for a job she knew nothing about. Or she could spend her evening preparing for the interview and take the terrible resume with her.

She called at 2 p.m. the next day and said she had a terrific interview. They liked her and she liked them. In fact, she was hired and would start work Monday.

"What about your resume?" we asked.

"Oh, that," Margie said. "Well, I folded the damn thing up and stuffed it in my purse. When the interview was over, one of the men took me to the

personnel department to fill out all the
forms to start work. We shook hands
there, and, as he was leaving, he
turned and asked if I had a resume
with me. I about died inside, but I said
I did. I reached into my purse and
without unfolding it, handed it to him.
He took it from me, handed it directly
to the personnel person and said, 'Here.
File this.' And then he was gone."

This is the tale of most resumes. ***They are needed for
a file.***

### SUMMARY:

Most of us hate working up a resume. It's rare when you
hear anyone say, "Boy! I had a wonderful weekend. I
stayed home and worked on my resume!"

You may get a job without a resume. If the people you
interview with know you and like you, they won't need a
resume — unless, of course, it's to satisfy company policy
and the human resource department. In the New Way job
search, the human resource department, most times, is the
last stop in the process.

### TRUTH #9

**A successful job search is 10 percent analytical
(technique, strategy) and 90 percent emotional (how
you feel about yourself and your ability to relate to
the rest of the world).**

How you put yourself out there — information interviews, job interviews, Busybodying — is more important
than being technically correct.

People hire people they know and like. What is likable?

What qualities do you enjoy in people? How about warmth, humor, sincerity, enthusiasm, compassion, integrity, assertiveness, openness, energy, thoughtfulness? How would you like to work with people who possess these qualities? Your workdays would be comfortable and exciting. Not a bad combination.

Are you exhibiting your best qualities to others as you do your job search? Or, are you tentative, bland and impersonal? Some job seekers appear "efficient" because they are scared to death, don't know what they are doing or feel unworthy and desperate. How would you like to work with people who possess *these* qualities?

Put yourself in the interviewer's shoes. Who would you hire? You certainly would not take much time with someone possessing the "efficient" set of qualities.

People tend to forgive a lot of technical mishaps (a forgotten appointment, a word misspelled on a proposal, a missed follow-up note or phone call) if they have respect for the job seeker. Yes, *respect for the job seeker.* If you do a New Way job search, and you follow all the rules, people will respect you. Some will envy your opportunity to thoroughly research the market to find a job you enjoy. They may genuinely want you to keep in touch with them because they are curious about what you're doing, how you're doing it, and where you will end up. They will want to help in any way they can.

On the other hand, it can be difficult to respect someone who never makes a mistake, but exhibits little warmth or personableness. People may wish you well in a ho-hum sort of way, but they will not feel *a part of* your job search. If they never hear from you again, they won't wonder about you. You are, in other words, quite forgettable.

What to do? Begin putting your *self* out there, warts and all. Let people in on who you are, your uniqueness. Exhibit professionalism in your job search along with your positive personal qualities. Engage people as you do your Stage II research.

You will begin to understand the graciousness of the human spirit. It will be demonstrated by those who spend time with you, advise you, and give you referrals and leads because they want you to succeed.

### SUMMARY:

Take a good look at your behavior. Are you likable, personable, interesting? Are you competent with your job search techniques? Are you putting your *self* out there? Do people respond to you positively?

Are you dressing well? Do you have decent clothes that make a favorable impression? If not, are you making efforts to update clothes, make-up, jewelry, or hair style? If you have a beard, does it look good on you? Is it trimmed at all times?

Is your networking notebook up and running? Do you have business cards? Are you keeping a calendar so as not to miss appointments? Are you sending thank-you notes?

Most importantly, is your job search interest-driven? Are you talking to people about things that are genuinely exciting to you? You see, the warmth, sincerity, humor, openness and energy come only when you have taken yourself seriously and are exploring interests that fit your uniqueness.

If you can answer "yes!" to all of the above, you probably feel good about yourself and how you relate to the rest of the world. You are ready to do a successful New Way job search — 90 percent ready.

The 10 percent will take care of itself. You will know when to analyze and strategize as you gather information that requires action. You will do whatever the situation requires.

Just put your *self* out there!

## TRUTH #10
**Whatever you believe to be the truth about the job market probably isn't.**

### Assumption 1.
We see people at CareerMakers who, after 10, 20 even 30+ years have been let go from companies through no fault of their own (mergers, buy-outs, downsizing — aka "rightsizing"). Most do not feel kindly toward their former employers.

Their assumption is that companies owe people jobs until retirement. Well, job security may have existed before 1980, but it is non-existent today. To assume that a job is forever is to create your own misery, a life riddled with fear of job loss, depression and helplessness.

The truth is the job market is dynamic, ever changing, even volatile. To be responsive to this job market, *you* must become dynamic, able to effect change for yourself whenever you want to or have to. Learn the New Way job search so you have the ability to change jobs *at will and without panic.* Your job security lies not in your present job or company, but in your ability to master the New Way job search.

**CASE IN POINT:**
Homer, 55, had been with a high-tech company for 27 years. Through drastic downsizing, he lost his job, but was hired back on contract for a special project. Three years later, Homer was out of work again.

Homer came to CareerMakers and became a networker "extraordinaire." He talked with all sorts of people in all sorts of companies, learned a lot and thoroughly enjoyed himself. He came across an opening on the Worker's Compensation Board, and, after letting the right people know he was interested, was appointed to a position with a three-year tenure.

Three years is just about up. Homer feels good about the last three years, *and is looking forward to another job search.* He believes he has a lot to contribute, and will find the right place to make his contribution. Retirement? Well, maybe, but maybe not.

Work is fun when you doing what you enjoy with people who appreciate your contribution. Such a dynamic person could die happy on the job. Just think about that and while you're at it, rethink your assumptions about the meaning of work and retirement.

**ASSUMPTION 2.**
We all make assumptions about the job market with regard to what's "out there." We assume, for example, that we know what it's like to work in banking, though we've never worked in the industry. After all, my neighbor works at a bank and he's not happy, so I certainly don't want to work at one.

Conversely, sometimes we covet the notion of working at a company that has a dynamic image, one glamorized in the press as state-of-the-art and a great place to work. We think, "Gee. I would love to work at W.W. Widgets." We have seen people make themselves miserable romanticizing about a company without ever Researching with a human being who works there!

Understanding the truth about what's out there comes from the informational interviewing connected with Researching. Banking might become exciting to a person who assumes it's not after some structured and directed talks with people who enjoy it. And a wishful thinker might discover from unhappy W.W. Widget employees that the company is more glamorous to read about than work for.

In our experience, as many people want to get out of a company as those who want to get in.

In point of fact, none of us knows the reality of the job market until we begin to talk to people in companies, industries and job titles other than our own.

CASE IN POINT:

Kathy, 28, was let go when her company no longer needed geologists. At CareerMakers she identified a strong interest in movies. She was intrigued by them and how they came into being. She went to all the new ones as soon as they came out.

Very slowly, Kathy began to take this interest seriously. She started talking with people in Portland's movie industry — right, not too many of those types in Portland. Then, on referrals from Portland people, she went to Seattle and did Researching there. She heard consistently that she needed to be in Los Angeles.

Logically, Kathy had nothing to offer the movie industry — she was, after all, a geologist. But its emotional pull was strong, indeed, and she didn't deny it. She went to Los Angeles and did information interviewing in the television and movie industries.

Yes, in reality she would probably start at an access level position. Yes, reality was she had a lot to learn. Yes, reality was that she would have a long road to a "successful" position. Yes, she was terrified thinking about leaving a profession that paid her $40,000.00 the year before.

Yes, she did it! Kathy landed a job with a well-known Los Angeles production company. Her earnings were cut in half, but, because the demons of enthusiasm, energy, aliveness and fun possessed her, she didn't much care.

### ASSUMPTION 3.
Yes, but -- I can't do what these other people have done. *I'm different*.

The only difference between you and the people illustrated in CASES IN POINT is that they have learned to be dynamic human beings. They are ordinary people who have taken themselves and their lives seriously, identified their uniqueness and developed the skills to do a New Way job search.

- They know who they are.
- They know what they want.
- They know how to get it.

### SUMMARY:
It's all there for you, too. It's just a matter of deciding to take yourself seriously and open up to new ways of operating in the world. The rest is "doing it."

Chapter II

## NEW WAY JOB SEARCH:
## THE GRACIOUS ART OF NETWORKING

### HOW *NOT* TO GET A JOB

Out of work? Want to change jobs? Just wait until the Sunday paper arrives. In it you will find the truth of the job market. And, you can do your job search without leaving the comfort of your home. Just stay in your pajamas, brew a fresh pot of coffee and decide your future based on the 1" x 3" ads in the Help Wanteds. Decide which job titles fit best this week. Send a slew of resumes to those human resource departments. Wait to be called for interviews. Finally, of course, choose a new job from the many offers that will come pouring in.

Sound familiar? It might be what you are doing now to land a job. And you probably do not feel good about the results. This kind of conventional, old way job search simply does not produce results for most people.

In fact, if you are currently engaged in this old way job search, you could be frustrated, angry, anxious and depressed. You may be seriously questioning your self-worth and competence. In other words, the old way job search also is hazardous to your mental health.

Plainly speaking, it's obsolete. It just doesn't work for most of us. Yet, we keep at it because we don't know what else to do.

## THE NEW WAY JOB SEARCH

The New Way job search involves learning new skills and new ways of thinking. Whenever we learn new skills and new ways of thinking, we must un-learn old habits of behavior and thought. This isn't easy and can cause anxiety as we replace the old with the new.

The anxiety begins with the understanding that the New Way job search is *not* about job titles. It is *not* about resumes. It is *not* about human resource departments. It is *not* about the Sunday want ads. It is *not* about the safety and comfort of your home.

The New Way job search *is* about you and what interests you. It *is* all about enthusiasm and excitement. It *is* about researching the job market to find where you want to work. It *is* about creating your job and naming it yourself. It *is* about human beings helping other human beings. It *is*, bottom line, about satisfaction and fulfillment on the job.

## A NETWORKING PROCESS: THE WORLD IS NOT FLAT

The New Way job search is a structured and directed networking process that, ultimately, helps you make wise career decisions and end up in satisfying work. Networking, as applied to the job search, requires a specific and sophisticated set of skills which *none of us has been taught* in junior high, senior high or college. The basic skill that needs to be learned is that of extending — putting your *self* into the world as an explorer to discover what's "out there."

Think about Columbus who, in the face of general assumptions about the earth's shape, sailed off to see for himself — extended his *self* out there. Columbus would not have proved to everyone that the earth was round and that new lands existed if he had stayed at home in safe, comfortable Portugal and applied for easy duty. A resume could have landed him a steady job in shipping and trading, sailing the same old seas. He would have been bored silly. No challenge. No risk. No fulfillment. Ho-hum.

As you participate in your own discovery process, you will be amazed and energized at what you learn about Christopher's round world and the possibilities it holds for you. Your New Way job search will open up new worlds for you just as it did for CareerMakers' graduates illustrated in Chapter I's CASES IN POINT.

### EXTENDING YOUR SELF

Developing the skill of extending is critical because you probably know very little about the world beyond your own boundaries. If you go to work at a company each day, you probably know a lot about that company. However, you may know precious little about the inner workings of other companies. Yet you have constructed ideas in your head about other companies, or industries, and you believe them to be truth. Most of these "truths" about the job market are not true at all. They are assumptions.

**Tough Reality:** If you have never done it, you may not have the vaguest idea what it is like to show up to work at another company. So, too, in other industries, you do not know what opportunities exist for you because you have not researched those possibilities. You do not know what it means to show up to a job other than your own because you have not talked with people in a specific way to find out what such a job is all about.

**Tender Reality:** Because we teach life planning and job search skills to people, it does not follow that we know the reality about other companies, industries and job titles. We are ignorant of most of the rest of the work world beyond the boundaries of CareerMakers. We know only about companies, industries and job titles that have been part of our pasts. This is the truth for all of us.

And so, it is hazardous to your future and your potential fulfillment to operate on assumptions about the job market. When you do, you cut yourself off from endless opportunity, and, you are likely to stay where you are: stuck in an unsatisfying job or an unsatisfying job search.

When do you "un-stuck" yourself? When do you take your *self* seriously and check out the reality of the work world?

When you are sick to death of showing up to your present job, or you are told not to show up, or you feel restless and wonder if there isn't something more exciting out there for you. Or perhaps you are searching for a job now, and you are not making progress.

You are ready to learn a reliable extending process *when you want to move,* and not before.

## TYPICAL QUESTIONS
Q. Do I network in order to get a job?
A. Immediately, no. Ultimately, yes.

Q. What does that mean?
A. It means that, immediately, you are talking to people in a research mode, exploring companies or industries or jobs of interest to you. You do this to make informed decisions about what you want to do next.

Q. Sort of checking things out?
A. Yes. That way you learn the reality of companies and

industries. You give yourself solid information on which to make decisions. You are no longer ignorant of what's "out there." You no longer make assumptions about jobs or career fields — you *know.*

Q. O.K. So where's the job?
A. While researching the job market you will contact many people. When you decide what you want to do, and let those people know of your decision, they will help you get to the people who have the power to hire.

Q. So, ultimately, the people I contact while doing my research will help me get to job openings when I decide what I want?
A. That's how it works.

Q. Are people really willing to talk about their jobs and companies? ·
A. Yes, they are. In fact, people are quite willing to help if you follow the rules of networking.

Q. There are rules?
A. You bet. And you must learn them so you can go about the process in a credible and professional manner.

Q. This sounds like nothing I've ever done before. I feel uncomfortable. Do other people feel this way?
A. Yes. Most people are uneasy with networking when they first hear about it. But most of us have done it successfully before and perfected the skills. We just haven't called it networking.

Q. What do you mean?
A. Here's a story that you may be able to relate to. Suppose you received a check from your Aunt Tillie for $18,000. Her note said that you had to spend it on a new

car. You could add to the amount if you wished, but you could not buy a new car for less than the $18,000. Tell me how you would feel about that.

Q. How would I feel? I'd be ecstatic! WOW! I couldn't wait to start looking for the new car.
A. Right. Tell me how you would decide on which car to buy.

Q. How would I decide which car to buy? I'd go to the library and read *Consumer Reports* to research the kinds of cars available. I'd look at ones that excited me, and check out their performance, features and economy. Then I would visit dealerships and kick some tires, collect brochures and ask a lot of questions. I'd drive some cars too. I'd also be on the lookout for the models I liked and talk to owners in parking lots if I could. When I had enough information, I would make my decision and hand over Aunt Tillie's check. Then roar off into the sunset!
A. Yep. You'd be sure you knew what you wanted before you parted with the check. Pretty smart shopping, I'd say. Well, you bring your unique skills and values into the job market — that's your $18,000 — and you want to do thorough research to make an informed decision on where to contribute those skills and values. Before you surrender yourself to a company to do a job, you want to make sure you're getting the right thing. You do research to find the company you want to hire.

Q. Wait a minute. Don't companies hire people?
A. That's the way it was. However, the New Way job search allows you to target and go after the job and company you want. When you get it, you have, in effect, hired your company.

Q. That's a whole new way to think about the job

search. Pretty exciting! How does it work?

A. By learning the skills of Busybodying, Researching and Generating Job Interviews.

## THE BRIDGE METHOD

When you want to make a job or career change— or you have to — you may feel as though you are on the brink of an abyss. You can see the other side, see where you want to be, but you don't know how to get there. Somehow, you need to build a BRIDGE across the abyss.

The BRIDGE method is useful in any life situation that requires additional knowledge to make an informed decision. The BRIDGE method is a survival tool with universal practicality. The focus here, however, is the job search process.

As you study the BRIDGE model on the next page, you will see three basic steps must be taken for a job or career transition. They are Busybodying, Researching and Generating Job Interviews. The three steps together form the networking process of a New Way job search. If undertaken with diligence and tenacity, they will pave the road to a new, better, fantastic job — WHEW!

We will look at each of these steps as a specific career management method.

But first . . .

### TAKE YOURSELF SERIOUSLY

Before you begin the BRIDGE process, you must get in touch with your interests, skills, and values. This means taking yourself, particularly your interests, seriously. The job search that ends with work that is enjoyable, satisfying, maybe even fun, is a journey that is interest-driven.

Your exploration of the job market (Researching) should be energizing and stimulating. Your enthusiasm should build as you talk with people who share your interests.

At this time you may have a lot of "yes, buts . . ." to overcome. Your self-talk may sound like this:

> "Yes, but . . . I've been an engineer for fifteen years."

> "Yes, but . . . my degree is in American History. I should use it somehow."

> "Yes, but . . . I already know all about computers. I should stick with what I know."

> "Yes, but . . . let's get real here. So what if I love tennis. I've been in banking for twenty years, and I need to make a living. I can't make a living in tennis."

**Tough Reality:**

Harold Kushner's book, *When All You've Ever Wanted Isn't Enough*, makes a deafening point about the above "yes, buts . . ." Kushner says that because of our fear of change "we choose lives of emotional flatness."

Just imagine you have an emotional oscilloscope. You can plug it in and take a reading any time. What would the line on your oscilloscope look like? Would it be a strong, rhythmic, flowing line with a broad range of regular highs and lows? If so, it would indicate a generally healthy enthusiasm for life with some wonderful peak experiences as well as some utterly miserable ones.

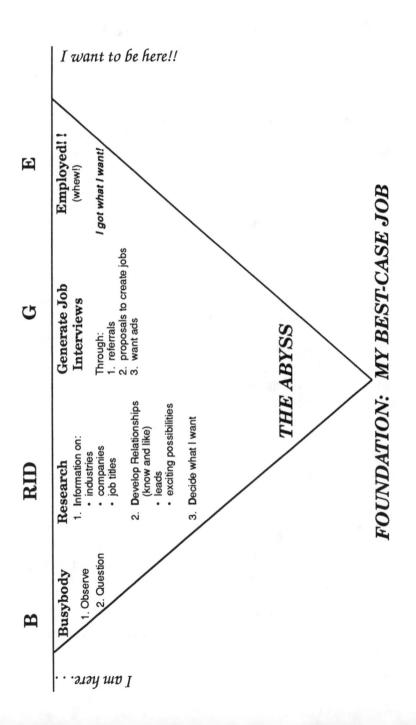

*I want to be here!!*

**B**    **RID**    **G**    **E**

**Busybody**
1. Observe
2. Question

**Research**
1. Information on:
   - industries
   - companies
   - job titles
2. Develop Relationships (know and like)
   - leads
   - exciting possibilities
3. Decide what I want

**Generate Job Interviews**
Through:
1. referrals
2. proposals to create jobs
3. want ads

**Employed!!**
(whew!)
*I got what I want!*

*THE ABYSS*

*FOUNDATION: MY BEST-CASE JOB*

*I am here...*

Or, would the line on your oscilloscope be weak and erratic — mostly flat — with an occasional blip indicating a dash of excitement? ("Oh yes. I remember that blip. That was when I played tennis last July.")

Most of us are emotionally flatlined when it comes to our work. We are bored. We yearn for fulfillment. We yearn for excitement. We are beat down by what we do, yet we stay where we are. We fool ourselves by rationalizing that we really have no choice.

But we choose to have emotionally flatlining jobs. One or several of the following excuses will probably fit your circumstances:

- You might not like your job, but you stay because you are addicted to security. If you leave, you may not get your regular pay-check fix with money, medical benefits and pension plan. The thought of withdrawal conjures visions of convulsions and hallucinations. So you choose the real pain of staying over the imagined pain of leaving.

- The very thought of letting go of the security and comfort of what you know — even if you hate it or are bored stiff by it — scares you to death.

- You might rationalize about yourself. You say things like, "Yes, but . . . it's not really so bad. My ulcers don't bother me too much, and I enjoy playing tennis on the weekend."

- Your rationalizations extend to the job market. "There's nothing out there for me at my age."

- You could be in denial of your very self. You may never have taken time to figure out what you're all about. Therefore, you are blind to your specialness. And so, you throw it away. You don't take yourself seriously as a human being with unique traits, skills and values to contribute to the world.

- You don't know how to explore the myriad of possibilities that, in reality, exist for you in the world of work.

What is the result of choosing a life of emotional flatness? Some day you will be looking back on your life. What do you want to say about your time on the planet?

> "Well, I'm 80. I wish I had done things differently. I spent a lot of time doing things that weren't interesting to me or of much value to anyone else. If only..."

> Or, "Well, I'm 80. By and large, I feel good about my life. I enjoyed my work and feel as though it was important to others, too. There's not much I would change if I could do it over again. I'm satisfied with myself."

### Tender Reality:

Most of us are not thoughtful about the lives we live. We show up to the same old workplace for the wrong reasons. We show up because we have failed to realize that our skills, traits and values are portable. We can pack them up and move them into just about any situation we choose.

## Do Your Homework

To get in touch with your interests, skills and values , turn to Chapter III, Homework. Spend time working on the exercises and assimilating the information on your Best-Case Job Summary Sheet (p. 107).

To take your interests seriously, reflect on what has meaning for you — the things you like — that you enjoy being around — *that engage both your heart and your mind.*

Then, when you are ready to begin a job search or career exploration, use the Focus Sheet (p. 109) and get going!

## Next: Go To The Store

To do a professional and credible job search, you must be prepared with the tools of the trade.

First, buy a Networking Notebook to keep track of people with whom you do information interviews. The notebook is a three-ring binder that is roughly 7" X 9". Buy paper to fit (5 1/2" X 8 1/2"), a set of dividers, and alpha tabs. Label dividers with your areas of interest. Alpha tabs are for the folks you meet who don't quite fit in with your interests, but are contacts nonetheless. If you already use an organizer, give thought as to whether you want to incorporate your job search materials into it. Most people find that a separate binder works best.

Refer to the Networking Notebook Samples in Appendix B for examples of how to set it up for your job search.

Buy a calendar, preferably one small enough to fit into the inside pocket of your notebook. It should have sufficient room on each day to write appointments easily.

Buy personal business cards. Consider them "confetti" and remember to shower them on those you meet in your job search.

Your cards should be printed on decent stock with your name, address and phone *ONLY*. Anything else, except perhaps a general sort of logo, limits you in a job search. Yes, your brand new MBA or Ph.D, contrary to what you may think, does not necessarily open up the world to you. It, in fact, may close doors. Your ideal job may not require such a degree, and when people see that you have one, they may dismiss you out of hand. However, if you think your degree might open some doors, get two sets of cards: one with, one without.

*You can not possibly be professional and credible in your search without business cards.*

Buy "Thank-you" notes. Choose ones that reflect who you are. Make sure you will be comfortable mailing them to people in your network. (More later on how to write them.)

Now you have what you need to do a New Way job search and are ready to carry out the three stages of networking.


## STAGE I NETWORKING: BUSYBODYING

Look back at the BRIDGE model (p. 41). You will see that the first step onto the BRIDGE is Busybodying. To take Busybodying seriously is to understand that you don't know where your next job is coming from. However, what you do know for certain is: *your job will come through other people.* Who? You don't know that yet. That's why it is critical that you do not make judgments about other people, or decide not to talk to someone because he/she is not in your "career field." When you get judgmental, you may not talk to people unless you think they can "do you some good." This is when networking becomes manipulative. In fact, you do not know who can be helpful until *after* you have talked with them. So, you must talk with all kinds of people, everywhere.

Busybodying is easy because you can do it wherever you find yourself: in line at the movies, at cocktail parties, at your child's soccer games. To Busybody effectively, you must simply make an observation on something relevant to the situation, and talk about it. Then proceed with the conversation (or not), depending upon the responsiveness of the other person. You are, in effect, conducting "friendly assaults" on the rest of humanity.

## TYPICAL QUESTIONS

Q.: Wait a minute! Are you saying that I should strike up a conversation with strangers?

A.: That's exactly what I'm saying. Remember, your job will come from and through another person. It could come from the person in the movie line just as easily as from a company president. It is your fear and assumption that make this possibility unbelievable.

Q.: Yeah, well, I'm a "meat and potatoes" person. I like to get down to business. This Busybodying is silly. How can it have anything to do with a job search?

A.: Busyboding is directly related to the job search in three ways:

> 1. It gives you practice talking with all sorts of new people. The practice will make you much more at ease during both information and job interviews.

2. It allows you to uncover job leads.

3. It helps you expand your network by getting names of people to talk to in companies and industries that are of interest to you.

Q.: O.K. I can see how Busybodying can make it easier to talk with new people. How does it uncover job leads?

A.: Very directly. Here's a true story: A fellow finished skiing for the day. As he was putting his skis on his car to go home, he observed another skier doing the same thing. Our fellow said, "It's a lot more fun taking them off the car to go skiing than it is putting them on to go home, isn't it?"

> Skier: "Yes. That's true, (pause) but I don't have too far to go home. I live in town up here."
> Fellow: "Oh! And what do you do to earn a living?"
>
> Skier: "I'm the director of the museum."
> Fellow: "I love that place! You must enjoy your job."
>
> Skier: "Yes. I do. And what do you do?"
> Fellow: "I was caught in the downsizing at the bank. So I'm in a career exploration."
>
> Skier: "That must mean you have a financial background."
> Fellow: "Yes, I do."
>
> Skier: "Well, I'm going to be hiring a Development Officer. Why don't I put

the information about that job in the mail to you?"
Fellow: "That would be terrific! Here's my card."

Q.: Pretty convincing — BUT. . .
A.: Look, there are several points to consider here. One is that if our fellow had not opened his mouth and talked to a stranger, he would never have uncovered that possibility. That is the Prime Rule of the job search: *Open your mouth and talk to people*. Secondly, this job was not advertised — remember the "Hidden Job Market?" And, finally, if this "friendly assault" had ended with a job, our fellow would tell his friends, "You won't believe this, but I got my job in the parking lot at the ski resort!" The overriding point of it all is that *he created his own good luck by Busybodying*.

Q.: I get it now. So how does Busybodying help to expand my network?
A.: First, you strike up a conversation using the observing-commenting method. As the conversation progresses, you are usually asked, "And what do you do?"

Q.: I know. I hate that question. I'm not "doing" anything if I'm out of work. What do I say?
A.: You say the absolute truth, and you say it with enthusiasm: "I am in a career exploration. Right now I'm researching corporate training and the food industry. Do you know someone I could talk to in those industries?" More than likely, if there is rapport between the two of you, the person will offer a name or two for you to contact.

Q.: Hmmm. Then I call them up and . . .?
A.: Take the next step across the BRIDGE (Researching). Call for an information interview and begin investi-

gating the job market. But do not neglect your Busybody-ing. Get easy with it. Have fun with it, just as you would if you were buying that new car. See what happens. Learn from mistakes. Don't be judgmental. Bring an attitude of *Curious Objectivity* to your job search. Ask yourself before you speak, "I wonder what will happen this time?" Then, open your mouth and start creating your own good luck.

## STAGE II NETWORKING: RESEARCHING

Researching is a structured information-gathering process. It is a tool to use for discovering the reality of industries, companies and job titles that sound interesting to you. This information-gathering process enables you to:

1. Make decisions about what you want to do.
2. Develop relationships with people who will come to know and like you. *These are the people who will ultimately help you find or create your next job!*

The Researching process has definite steps, and you must follow them carefully. If you do not, you stand a good chance of losing credibility. A sloppy job search still gets people to know you. But they sure won't like you if you become obnoxious or fail to keep in touch, send "Thank Yous," or return things.

## RULES OF RESEARCHING

There are seven basic steps of Researching and, if you follow them, you will conduct a professional and credible job search:

1. Identify three areas of interest. (Chapter III, Homework, pp. 80-83.)

2. Identify five people you want to talk to in those areas of interest.
3. Call those people
4. Go see them
5. Say "Thanks"
6. Filter your information
7. ***Keep in touch with those people!!!***

The following pages explain each step. Read through them to get a comprehensive picture of the job search process. Then get specific with **your** Researching process. (Focus Sheet, p. 109.)

## 1. IDENTIFY THREE AREAS OF INTEREST

Remember that your job search should be enjoyable. It will be if you take your interests seriously. So, select three areas of interest that you would like to explore, be they industries, companies or job titles.

These three interests represent the starting point of your job search. You can add more interest areas as you progress with your career exploration, but this is where you begin.

## 2. IDENTIFY FIVE PEOPLE TO CALL FOR INFORMATION INTERVIEWS

Perhaps you already know people working in your areas of interest. If so, begin your career exploration with them.

If you do not know people in a certain industry, company, or job title, reach out to your friends and acquaintances — relatives, pastors, co-workers, neighbors — anyone you already know. Go to those people with whom you are most comfortable, those who are "warm," easy to be with. Ask if they know anyone in your areas of interest. They will, most likely, be happy to refer you to people so you can begin Researching.

### 3. CALL THOSE PEOPLE

Calling to make Researching appointments usually causes all sorts of anxiety. It is here that you come face-to-face with your fear of self-promotion. The phone call brings up the negative thinking about the process, and you are likely to resist, avoid and procrastinate.

The simple fact is this: resistance, avoidance and procrastination will prevent you from moving along in your exploration. If you do not pick up the phone, you will remain stuck.

To reduce anxiety and make Researching appointments, *prepare.* Use the Target the Call Sheet in Appendix B, p. 116.). This will help you focus on exactly what you want to say. Before you pick up the phone, write the appropriate information on the sheet.

Read the Target the Call Sheet from left to right and your conversation will sound like this:

> "Hello, Mike Green. My name is Jane Thomas. I am currently in a career exploration, and I'm interested in knowing more about the food industry. Shirley Quinn suggested I call because you have been in the industry for some time. I would like to talk with you for about twenty minutes on Tuesday or Thursday morning to learn more about the industry and whether or not it might match with my career interests."

- You have stated what you want clearly and succinctly: information.

- You have stated the boundaries: twenty minutes on Tuesday or Thursday.

Mike Green knows Shirley Quinn, so he will take your call seriously. And, since you are not asking for a job, he will not feel threatened by your request. In fact, he will probably welcome the opportunity to help you make career decisions.

If your request for an appointment is denied, it is usually because the person you want to see is genuinely tied up with a project, budgeting, going out of town on business or vacation. Ask if you can call back when things settle down. Also ask if you can talk with someone else in the meantime.

If you call and need to go through a secretary to see Mike Green, simply tell her/him what you want. *Stick to your agenda.*

## TYPICAL QUESTIONS

Q.: Are you telling me to call up perfect strangers?

A.: In a sense, yes. But in each case you have a referral. That is someone who knows the person you are calling. The referral is a link to your contact. You should always be able to say, "So-and-So suggested I call. She/he thought you might be helpful." Your referral insures success in getting the appointment 95 percent of the time.

Q.: How do I get started if my friends don't know anyone in my areas of interest?

A.: Remember the Prime Rule: Open your mouth and

talk to people! You see, when you identify your areas of interest, you enable yourself to become directed in your job search. Just tell everyone you see, "I'm doing a career exploration and would like to talk to people in the food industry." Then ask, "Do you know anyone I can talk with to find out more about it?"

Q.: Will these people give me names?

A.: Yes. They will give you names of people to call. People genuinely want to help.

Q.: OK. What about secretaries? How can I get past them?

A.: There is no way to "get past" the secretary. The only way is *through* the secretary. The secretary is paid to screen callers. Make friends with her/him. Do not state anything but the absolute truth about why you want to see Mike Green. Your conversation will go something like this:

> "Hello, my name is Jane Thomas, and I would like to talk with Mike Green."

> The secretary says, "And what is this in regard to?"

> "I am in a career exploration and a mutual friend, Shirley Quinn, suggested I call. I would like to talk with Mr. Green for about twenty minutes to gather some information on the food industry."

> "All right. You would like twenty minutes of Mr. Green's time?"

> "Yes. And it is very important that he

know that Shirley Quinn referred me to
him."

"I will give him the information and
call you back."

"That's great! If I haven't heard from
you by Friday (two days from the time
of the call), may I call you to see where
I stand?"

"Yes. That will be fine."

"Thank you very much!"

And, if you don't get a call back within two days, call to
see where your appointment stands. There is not a secretary worthy of the title who will not call you back.

Q.: Does it really work like this?
A.: Yes, it does. But you won't believe that until you
actually do it.

Q.: Any other hints?
A.: If you are conducting a full-time job search, make
five calls each day to get appointments for information
interviews. Five calls does not equate to five appointments. People are very hard to reach. But by making five
calls each day, you will always have your interviews
scheduled in advance, and you may get past feeling intimidated by the telephone. Five calls a day also means you
won't have to make fifteen calls all in one day to get five
appointments. That is pure misery. *Phoning is the key to
success of your job search.* No calls equals no Researching. If you call people and then go to see them, you are
definitely "doing it."

4.  **GO SEE THEM**
    **Do this:**
    > A. Go to your Networking Notebook and
    > **prepare** a page for each person you call.
    > (See Networking Notebook Sample, Appen-
    > dix B.)
    > B. **Prepare** your questions in advance. What
    > do you want to know about this person and
    > the industry or company?

If you are not certain about what to ask during the
Researching process, use the  starter questions below.
They are basic, but produce lots of useful information. As
you progress in your Researching  you will sense what you
actually need to know from people to make solid decisions
about what you want to do. **Get going with this agenda:**

> - How did you get where you are now? What
>   was your path to this job? What is your
>   education?
> - What is the purpose of your department/
>   job?
> - What aspects of your job give you the most
>   satisfaction?
> - What aspects of your job give you the least
>   satisfaction?
> - **What important issues or challenges
>   will you (or your department) face in
>   the next year?** (This question is key to
>   creating a job. See Proposals,  p. 68. )
> - What publications should I be reading?
> - Who else do you recommend I talk with?

**Don't do this:**
Never, ever, under any circumstances whatsoever —
no way — don't even think about it — nope — don't do it —

## NEVER TAKE A RESUME
## ON AN INFORMATION INTERVIEW!

Why? Well, you called and made an appointment to **get information.** Presenting a resume at an information interview says, "Yeah. Well. I said I wanted information, but what I really want is a job." A resume is all about **getting a job.** It has no place and serves no purpose whatsoever at an information interview. If you even so much as entertain the thought of sticking one in your Networking Notebook "just in case," you are confusing Stage II Researching with Stage III Generating A Job Interview.

The results are disastrous:
1. You lose credibility immediately. You asked for one thing on the phone (information). Now you want something else (a job). You do not appear to know what you want or what you are doing.
2. As soon as anyone has your resume, it is difficult, if not impossible, to continue to develop a relationship. The only question you can ask of those who possess your resume is, "Do you have any openings?" The answer is always, "Gee. No. We don't." Click.

What do you do with those "old way" people who expect you to have a resume with you? State quite truthfully, "I'm currently in the Research Stage of my job search, gathering information on your industry (company or job title). The information you give me today will help with my career decisions. I honestly don't know whether or not your industry is a fit for me. That's why I want to ask you some questions about it. Let's get going!"

When you say that, you convey that you know exactly why you are there and what you want. In short, you know what you are doing, and you are in control — *credibility plus!!!*

## BEING THERE

- Enter smiling. Extend your hand and say, "I'm Jane Thomas and I want to thank you for making time to see me."

- After exchanging pleasantries, say, "I have several questions to ask you. The answers will help me decide on a career path."

- Ask if you can take notes. Open your Networking Notebook, find Mike Green's page and your questions, and ask away!

- Keep track of time. Check in at about 15 minutes by saying, "We've been talking for fifteen minutes, and I have three more questions for you. We'd better move along."

- At the end of your time together, ask, "Who else would you suggest I talk with?" Then wind it up by saying, "Thank you for your time and referrals. If I have further questions, may I call you?"

- Collect a business card from Mike Green and offer him one of yours. Tape his card to his page in your Networking Notebook. As you become familiar with this process, you will begin to realize that you are in complete control. You make the call. You prepare the agenda for the meeting. You take responsibility for keeping to task and time. You end the interview.

## 5. SAY "THANKS"

Write a "Thank You" note within 48 hours of your appointment. Make it meaningful. Use this three-paragraph approach:

A. Say something like, "Thank you for taking time to meet with me yesterday."

B. State *something specific* that you learned from the interview. Let Mike Green know that you were listening. This tells him that his time was well spent. For example, "It was interesting to learn your views on working out of your home. I will re-think my views on that in light of your experience."

C. The only way that people can come to like you is through repeated contact. In this last paragraph of your note, tell Mike Green that you will keep in touch. Speak of referrals, "I will let you know how my meetings with Sally and Bill turn out." Or, "I will call as I have more specific questions."

Remember this about saying "Thanks." The people who see you are operating out of a generosity of spirit. *They will expect the same from you.* Saying thanks is your way of returning kindness to those who are gracious enough to help you with your career exploration.

The best notes are those that are handwritten rather than typed. Handwritten notes are of a more personal, warm nature. Since you are developing relationships with people, the warm touch with "Thank You" notes is preferable to the "business" approach.

Buy your "Thank You" notes at any store that has a stationery department. Select ones you like — that reflect who you are. Then you will enjoy sending them out.

## 6. FILTER YOUR INFORMATION

What do you do with the information that you gather? Filter it through your Best-Case Job Summary Sheet, which contains the essentials of what you want in a job. Sit down with your Summary Sheet and get thoughtful about what you have learned and what you want in a job.

**Filtering Questions:** Ask yourself the following questions and write the answers in your networking notebook.

- What did I learn about the industry or company or job?
- What specific challenges or issues will be faced in the next year? Am I intrigued by them? Why? Why not?
- How excited am I by the prospect of working in this industry or company or job? Use a scale of 1-10.
- How does what I learned fit with my Summary Sheet? Skills, interests, people, etc.
- What conclusions can I draw at this point? What are my next steps? How do I move on?
- Could I write a proposal to create a job?

It is necessary to carry out this filtering exercise to make sense of the information you are gathering. If you do not, your information will not lead you to the "next steps" in the process.

*It is through this thoughtful filtering that you enable yourself to analyze and strategize what you need to do to keep moving in the process.*

## 7. KEEP IN TOUCH WITH THOSE PEOPLE!!!

People hire people they know and like. *To like or be liked takes repeated contact.* Ask yourself: Would you refer someone for a job interview that you met once for twenty minutes? Probably not. It is critical to develop relationships with people who are gracious enough to see you in the first place.

Develop relationships with people you genuinely like. Do not think you have to cultivate relationships with those who have power and influence. When and if you need access to powerful and influential people, those with whom you have developed relationships while Researching will help you get in touch with them.

### Methods for Keeping In Touch

• Call and thank people for referrals. This is a 90 second call and could be the best thing that happens to someone all day:

> "Hello, Mike. This is Jane Thomas. I
> want to thank you for referring me to
> Sally Peters. We met yesterday, and I
> learned a lot. She's a warm and helpful
> person."

• Call and ask additional questions. The more people you talk with, the more questions you raise. Don't be bashful. Call and get the information you need to make decisions. Remember, you already asked if you could call with additional questions at the end of your information interviews.

• Go to the mail. Send things of interest, such as cartoons, or articles you think a person would like.

• Return things. You asked about publications. Often people will lend you materials to read. Return them with a "Thank You." If there are things you would like to discuss, make another appointment.

• Determine sounding boards. As relationships grow and develop, identify people with whom you have rapport. Because they have a genuine interest in helping, they are easy to call. Coffee, lunch or dinner are options now. And, given the chance, they will act as mentors or advisors.

• When keeping in touch with people, do so within the bounds of the job search. As you get to know people, you might move out of job search boundaries into areas of sociability.

One thing to remember: People will develop a true curiosity about you and your search. They will watch your activities with interest, and wonder where you will end up. And so, the worst question anyone can ask about you is, "Whatever happened to Jane Thomas?" If this question is being asked about you, you are not conducting an effective search — you're simply not networking.

## YOUR TRAIL OF CREDIBILITY

When you follow the seven steps of Researching, you will leave a trail of credibility. You will be conducting a professional job search. People will respect and admire you. This is important because *the way you conduct your job search is the way you are perceived as a prospective employee:*

> • When you call people back and thank them for referrals, you exhibit follow-through and assertiveness.

- When you send a "Thank You" you exhibit sincerity.

- When you appear for your information interview with a networking notebook, business cards and agenda, you exhibit preparedness and professionalism.

- When you call and ask additional questions, you exhibit persistence.

- Through the job search, you are showing people that you are thoughtful and competent — you know what you're doing.

*You project the exact characteristics of a dedicated and enthusiastic employee, just what managers are looking for.*

## TYPICAL QUESTIONS

Q.: There's a whole lot more to this networking process than I thought. I'm overwhelmed. Do other people feel this way?

A.: This kind of thorough networking process is new to most people. When they are first exposed to it, they feel overwhelmed. It is a lot to assimilate, especially when most people know so little about networking in the first place. The fact of the matter is, *people simply do not know how to network effectively.* It takes commitment, courage, energy and organization. Most of all, you must follow the rules as presented here.

Q.: I can see that. It seems to me that it will take a long time to get to the other side of that abyss. How long does it take to do all this research, make a decision and get the job?

A.: Here's an answer you don't want to hear. How long it takes depends upon you and exactly how much commitment you bring to your job search. We know you must talk to between eight and 15 people in each area of interest to gather enough information to make solid career decisions. But think about it. If you were to get serious and talk to six people a week, in 10 weeks you could talk to 60 people in your areas of interest. When is the last time you talked with 60 people in 10 weeks to research the job market?

Q.: Never. It sounds like a lot of work though. Are you absolutely sure my ideal job won't appear in the Sunday paper?

A.: I'm 99 percent positive. And, yes, extending yourself into the world requires hard work. But, it's also lots of fun. You are talking with people who share your interests. Look at your job search as an adventure. Then pick up the phone and begin the process. Your energy level and enthusiasm will soar as you begin talking to people in your areas of interest. You will come alive as you search for your job. You will, undoubtedly, uncover possibilities you didn't know existed.

Q.: I can see that. I must admit, this is getting interesting. Is there a final word on the process?

A.: The final word is this: there is no shortcutting the process. If you just make calls, go see people, and write "Thank You" notes, you are not networking. You must keep in touch with people in your network. You must develop relationships. Only then will you create solid relationships with people who will come to know you, like you and, ultimately, help you get the job.

Q.: I see. What's next?

A.: Making decisions on the things you want to do.

## DECIDING WHAT YOU WANT TO DO

The researching process enables you to decide what you want to do. It is important to understand that you may uncover more than one possibility. Therefore, do not think in terms of *"it."* Think in terms of *"them."* As you go about your New Way job search, you will find yourself thinking things like, "Hmm. I could do this. I could do that." This is your clue that the process is working. You are thoughtful about your research. You are sorting, discarding and keeping information that will help you decide what's next.

While you're taking what's going on in your head seriously, you must do the same with your belly. That's where your enthusiasm lives. What is grabbing your insides? When are you saying, "Boy! It would be fun to show up and do that!" Statements like that put you in touch with your passions — that which puts a "fire in your belly." Do not deny your passions. Explore every single possibility to work in a field that really excites you. Pay attention to the fire. Take your belly seriously.

After talking with people in your areas of interest, you may say, "Wow! I would love to work in this company." Or, you may decide "Phooey! I don't want to do that job." Because your information is from people who are working in your area of interest, your decisions are based on reality, not assumption. You are making informed decisions.

## WHEN YOUR DECISION IS "PHOOEY!"

Let's get back to an earlier example involving Mike Green and the food industry. After talking with Mike and about a dozen others related to the industry, you decide this is not for you. You just aren't excited about it. Your skills and values aren't in synch with what's needed. You decide that you have a clear picture of the reality of the food industry and — *Phooey!*

## MAKE THE DECLARATION

Call those who have been gracious enough to take time to talk with you and tell them your decision. Your conversation sounds something like this:

"Hello, Mike. This is Jane Thomas."

"Hi, Jane. How is the job search going?"

"It's going well. In fact, I have just made a major decision, and I want you to know about it. Do you have a minute to talk?"
"Yes. This is a good time."

"Well, as you know, I have been talking with a variety of people in the food industry. Based on the information I've gathered, I've decided that your industry isn't for me. It feels good to know that. I want to thank you for your help. I couldn't have made the decision without you."

"Well, then, what are you going to do?"

"As a matter of fact, I'm currently exploring corporate training and computer sales. I'll just bet you know some people I could talk to who are doing those things."

"You don't give up, do you? Well, as it happens, my sister is in corporate training at First Bank. She will probably talk with you. As for computer sales, no one comes to mind right now.

I'll think about that. Now let me give
you my sister's number."

"Thanks."

"You're welcome. To tell the truth, I
can't wait to see where you end up!"

When you share your decision with those in your
network, you let them know where you are in the process.
It also allows you to continue your networking.

**WHEN YOUR DECISION IS "WOW!"**
It's time for . . .

## STAGE III NETWORKING: GENERATING JOB INTERVIEWS

You have completed your Researching, the Stage II
Networking, and you now know what you want to do. It is
time to Generate Job Interviews (review BRIDGE model p.
41.) There are three basic ways to do this:

1. Referrals. Information on job openings will come
through the people with whom you have done Stage II
Networking. They will know and like you and will not have
any difficulty referring you for openings. You will probably
be interviewed for these positions.

2. Proposals. Information on job possibilities will come
to you through your Researching efforts. You may uncover
needs within companies and respond by writing a proposal
to create a job for yourself. When you call to present your
proposal, you are scheduling your own job interview.

3. Want ads, etc. Job openings are found in the Sunday
want ads, on company job hotlines, in company human

resources departments, at employment agencies, with headhunters and search firms. These usually demand a resume, which is put in the pile along with all the rest.

Let's look at the effectiveness of referrals, proposals and want ads as vehicles to generate job interviews.

## 1. REFERRALS

After talking with a dozen or so people in the food industry, you find that it's a match. You thoroughly enjoy being in industry-related companies. You like the environment. You see how your skills fit. Your head and belly are in agreement. Your head is thinking, "I could do this and this and this. Maybe even this!" And your belly is responding, "Right on! Really causes sparks down here!"

### MAKE THE DECLARATION

Call those who have been gracious enough to take time to talk with you and share your decision. Your conversation sounds something like this:

"Hello, Mike. This is Jane Thomas."

"Hi, Jane. How is the job search going?"

"It's going well. In fact, I have just made a major decision, and I want you to know about it. Do you have a minute to talk?"

"Yes. This is a good time."

"Well, as you know, I have been talking with a variety of people in the food industry. Based on the information I've gathered, I've decided that the industry is a good fit for me. Not only can I

make a contribution with my skills, I
am very excited about the prospect of
doing that. Talking with you and
others, I see how my skills transfer.
***I'm really ready to get a job now,***
and my next step is to get a piece of
paper together to illustrate those
skills—a resume or qualifications brief.
I want to make sure I'm on track.
When I get the rough draft together
would you critique it with me? I'd
appreciate your opinions and feedback."

"That is exciting! Sure, I'll take a look
at your rough resume. Call me when
you're ready."

"Thanks. I will."

Telling your decision to those who helped you allows
you to continue the process. Now, however, you are in
Stage III Networking. You must let the people with whom
you have developed relationships know that ***you now want
a job.*** Your resume tells people about your skills, enabling
them to refer you for leads and job openings with confidence in your abilities. You are a known quantity with a
great deal of credibility.

## 2. WRITING PROPOSALS TO GENERATE A JOB INTERVIEW

The only way you can write a proposal to create a job is
by Researching. The key question to ask at an information
interview is, "What issues or challenges will your company
be dealing with in the next year?"

The answer allows you to begin thinking of how you

might help meet those challenges. Match the "inside" information that you gather through Researching to your Best- Case Job Summary Sheet. If you are excited by the match, you are on your way to creating a brand new job.

Realistically, uncovering such possibilities may take more than one conversation. If the rapport is there, this won't be a problem. In fact, savvy employers will be interested in ideas that will make money, save money or save time.

### THE PROPOSAL FORMAT

Using the information you have gathered, you need to show, in focused terms, how your abilities will bring added value to the company. You need to present a strong and clear case that shows how your skills and efforts will bring money into the company.

To put your proposal in clear and concise terms, think about what you will do, how you will do it and the results the company can expect when you are hired.

### Get Thoughtful:

*What* will you do to help this person or company with issues or challenges?

*How* will you carry out what you want to do for the company? Clearly write the steps you will take to meet your objective(s).

*Results:* If you are given the opportunity to make the contribution, what bottom-line results will the company see? How will you make money for the company, save it money, or save it time (which is money)? In the employer's words, "Why should I say 'yes' to your proposal? Why should I hire you? What's in it for me?"

This format provides the clarity and succinctness that busy people appreciate.

Now, sit down with the information, blank sheets of paper and begin a rough draft. You need three columns, or three sheets of paper, with the headings:

| What I Will Do | How I Will Do It | Results |
| --- | --- | --- |
| | | |

This is the same format you developed in writing Skill Stories in Chapter III, **Homework**). Just project yourself into the future instead of recounting the past.

### PREPARING YOUR PROPOSAL

After you have roughed out a proposal, you must put it in "deliverable" form. This means:

- Having someone proof the proposal for clarity, grammar, and spelling.
- Writing a cover letter that tells why you have written the proposal.
- Including a resume supporting your abilities to do what you have proposed — if appropriate.
- Buying a cover folder.
- Copying your proposal on good quality paper.
- Assembling your proposal:
    1. Cover letter
    2. Proposal
    3. When appropriate, resume.

## PRESENTING YOUR PROPOSAL: ARRANGING YOUR INTERVIEW

# NEVER MAIL YOUR PROPOSAL!

Call the person to whom you will present the proposal. Tell him/her that you have worked hard to put a proposal together. This probably will not come as a surprise if you have talked with the person several times already. Express your enthusiasm and talk in terms of "win-win" benefits.

Your conversation will sound something like this:
"Hello, Mike. This is Jane."

"Hello, Jane. How are you?"

"Actually, I'm terrific! I'm calling because I have done a lot of thinking about the conversations we've had concerning the issues your company will be addressing next year. I'm pretty sure I can make a contribution, and I have written a proposal outlining my ideas. I would like to share it with you. Can we make a time to meet?"

"Sure. How about Tuesday at 1:30?"

"That's good. I'll see you then. Is there anyone else who might be there? If so, I'll bring additional copies."

"Yes, I'd like Anne to sit in with us. You might bring a copy for her."

"I'll do that. See you Tuesday!"

"I'm looking forward to it."

When you present your proposal, you will be talking with someone you already know and who already knows you. You will also know about the company, its environment and the people who work there. You will know how your skills, values and interests fit with the organization. Your proposal, then, becomes your job description.

The power in the proposal process lies in your ability to write your own job description and arrange your own job interview. This is possible only through the methods of the New Way job search.

### EXPECTATIONS

Do not expect to be hired on the spot when you present the proposal. Your first presentation will let people know what you can do for them, how you will do it and the results expected if they hire you. But, as familiar as your proposal is to you (you have lived, eaten and breathed it), it's all new to the people at the presentation. People need time to think about new ideas.

After discussing your proposal, ask what "next steps" need to be taken. Or, "Where do we go from here?" Before you leave, make sure you have either a date to meet again or a day on which you call for another meeting. This is how you stay in control of the situation. Do not leave saying, "I look forward to hearing from you." If you do that, you give your control away.

### Yes , But . . .

You may say, "Yes, but . . . what if I write a proposal and they take it and have  someone else  implement it?"

That's the chance you take. The sin is to not write the proposal. If you don't, you will be rattling around miserably inside yourself saying something like, "Boy! I see an exciting possibility, but if I write it up they'll probably give it to somebody else."

This negative thinking keeps you stuck in your own "Woe-is-me!" attitude. Why make yourself unhappy? Write the proposal, and if it is not well received for whatever reason, accept that graciously and go on to the next possibility.

## 3. GENERATING JOB INTERVIEWS THROUGH WANT ADS, ETC.

This is the least effective way to generate job interviews. Responding to job openings that require resumes and all the accompanying information is, by and large, a cold, random process that produces few results.

People hire people they know and like. How is it possible to come to know and like you from a few pieces of paper that usually illustrate your past job history? And, if you have the necessary "qualifications" for the job opening and your resume speaks to those qualifications, so may every other resume in the stack. They are all basically the same! How in the world do personnel screeners make decisions on who to interview?

They use a process of de-selection. Anyone who is not a specific, cookie-cutter fit for the position is not considered.

Let's say that you fit the mold and are called for an interview. If you have not done Stage II networking and researched the company or industry, how informed are you about them? How can you even minimally prepare for the interview from a base of ignorance? How can you possibly come across as enthusiastic and dynamic when you are operating from a void of uncertainty?

Should you forget about responding to want ads? Well, if you are serious about getting a job, you will use every method available to you. However, every time you put a resume in the mail in response to an ad, picture it going into a black hole. Assume you will never hear a thing from that black hole — and get on with your Researching. That's where the action is. That's how you will, most likely, generate job interviews.

## TYPICAL QUESTIONS
Q.: If I do a New Way job search, I'm really in control from beginning to end, aren't I?

A.: Yes, you are. You are operating from a base of extraordinary personal power. You are competent. You no longer wait for things to happen so you can react. You make things happen. You become your own careermaker. Once you know the process, it becomes a way of life, and you realize that you can change jobs anytime you want to. You feel at peace with yourself and confident in the process.

Q.: It seems you're saying that the BRIDGE method moves people out of helplessness and dependency. Isn't it like kicking the habit of the old way to find a job?

A.: Exactly.

Q.: Whew! This is exciting and it makes sense. How come I'm feeling so uneasy . . . scared?

A.: It's hard to do things in new and different ways. You must stretch out of your comfort zone. In this case, you stretch right out into the abyss.

Q.: Boy! I guess! I'm trapped between knowing and

doing. If I choose not to do the New Way job search, I choose helplessness and unfulfillment. I stay stuck, don't I?

A.: Yes.

Q.: Any hints on taking the first tiny step onto the BRIDGE?

A.: The first tiny step onto the BRIDGE must be preceded by a giant leap.

Q.: A what?

A.: A giant leap — of faith.

Q.: Uh. Oh. Have I been hoodwinked into something?

A.: Not at all. It's just that as you embark upon this process, it is helpful to sort out your beliefs about people and how the world works.

Q.: I'm not clear on this. What do you mean?

A.: Take time to think about your basic beliefs.

## BASIC BELIEFS RELATED TO THE BRIDGE METHOD

First of all, ask yourself what you believe about what's fair. How do you feel when you hear that someone got a job because he or she knew the people who had the power to hire? After all, there were all those other "qualified" candidates who diligently did all the paperwork to get an interview, and they were barely considered. Does this upset you? If so, you might want to adjust your thinking, because you are buying into the belief that the old way — resumes, want ads, human resource departments — works. You might believe that only those who are most qualified get the jobs. This is not reality, whether or not you think it's fair.

Secondly, what is your basic belief about yourself?

Do you care enough about yourself to feel deserving of best-case work? Do you feel you deserve fulfillment from a job? If not, you might want to adjust your thinking. You are worthy, but, if you don't feel that you are you will not project a positive image.

Finally, how responsive do you think people will be to you as you conduct your job search? Do you believe people want to help you toward a new job? Or do you view people as small and mean and unwilling to talk with you? Do you believe that since "time is money" people will not want to see you for twenty minutes? Do you believe that it's a "dog-eat-dog" world in which you must make it on your own, or not at all? If you believe in the smallness of humanity, you might want to adjust your thinking. This belief will prevent you from taking your first step onto the BRIDGE. Who wants to pick up the phone and start the information interviewing process with the belief that people don't care and won't help?

If, indeed, these are your basic beliefs about the world and the people who inhabit it, but you have the overriding suspicion that the BRIDGE method just might work, test it. Make the leap. Call people. Go see them. Say "thanks." You will, without a doubt, be pleasantly surprised.

On the other hand, if you believe in the generosity of humanity, *you already have made the leap.* You may be uneasy and scared, but it is simply because the process is new to you and you don't want to make mistakes. No one does. However, if you believe people will treat you kindly — even if you don't do it quite right at first — you will pick up the phone.

The belief in generosity means you feel that most people respond to others with grace and compassion. And so, you believe that when you extend yourself, you will be met with grace and compassion. It is this generosity of spirit on the part of others that graciously allows for your mistakes and wishes you well. You see, tapping into the hidden job market means tapping into the enormous reservoir of generosity found in people.

Take the plunge! The water's warm!

## Chapter III

## HOMEWORK:

- **IDENTIFYING INTERESTS**

- **SKILLS AND SKILL SETS**

- **THE REST OF THE PICTURE**

- **YOUR BEST-CASE JOB**

- **FOCUS!**

### IDENTIFYING INTERESTS

A job search that ends with a new, better, fantastic job is interest-driven. So, interests provide the base of your job search. You will do Stage II Research to find a home for your skills and values in one of your interest areas. And when you have that wonderful job, you no longer will say, "Thank God it's Friday."

Take time to work through the following Interest Exercises. Write answers to each of the following questions once — then revisit the questions. Add information. Subtract information, whatever you feel is necessary. You might want to use separate paper.

When you are ready, choose *three* areas of interest you would like to explore with the Researching of Stage II Networking. Write those three areas of interest on your Best-Case Job Summary Sheet, p. 107.

## INTEREST EXERCISES

1. When you go into a book store, in which sections do you spend time browsing and reading? Aviation? Theology? Cooking? Make a list:

*HEALTH - PREVENTIVE, NUTRITION, EXERCISES ETC COOKING*

*HOME IMPROVMENT*

*CREATIVE - DESIGN HOME DEC CRAFTS ETC,*

2. What issues are you curious and/or passionate about? Feminism? Drunk driving? Prejudice? Make a list:

3. What occupies your thoughts? If you could have conversations with famous people, living or dead, who would they be? What would you talk about? Make a list:

*INTERESTING   WILLING TO SHARE,*
*CREATIVE   GENEROUS,*
*HELPFUl*
*TALENTED   TRAVELING*

4. Look around your house. What "things" do you have that you really like . . . your CD player, purses, pictures, tropical fish, cooking utensils, cosmetics, tools, furniture, clothes, etc. Make a list:

5. What would you do with yourself if you won the lottery? After the thrill was gone and you had indulged yourself, what would you do with your life?

*invest TAX FREE IRA RETIREMENT, PAY ALL ACCOUNTS In Full, Invest HOME Improvement #MAYBE NEW HOME, TRAVEL, EDUCATION, my childen, help celena Invest, RED CROSS those in need, my last expences*

6. What would you do with yourself if all your obligations were taken care of and you could do anything that you wanted to do *and you knew you would be a smashing success?*

*USE ALL MY GOD GIVEN TALENT BEING — CREATIVE MY ART*

7. Spiritually speaking, how would you use your God-given talents to make this planet/nation/society/state/city better than it is now?

## THE WONDER SHEET

To help identify interests further, ask yourself:

What do I wonder about?

What am I curious about?

What would I like to know more about?

I wonder what opportunities there are for me in these **industries:**

1. _____

2. _____

3. _____

I wonder what opportunities there are for me in these **companies:**

1. _____

2. _____

3. _____

I wonder what it means to be a . . . **job title:**

1. _____

2. _____

3. _____

Look back over the Interest and Wondering exercises. Stare into middle space and feel which interests come to mind. You may have to put this aside while your subconscious works on it.

Now, if you are going to begin a career exploration or job search *and you want to have fun doing it,* you will take exploring these three areas of interest seriously:

1. _____

2. _____

3. _____

Transfer these to your Best-Case Summary Sheet.

## SKILLS

The following three pages contain Skill Sets (**bold**). Under each Skill Set you will find words to describe skills used in that Skill Set.

**Suggestion:** Use a pencil to do your exercises. You will, no doubt, want to make changes before you commit the results to your Best-Case Summary Sheet.

1. Take your time, and look through all three pages of Skill Sets and skill words. Thoughtfully check each skill word that describes a skill you have used in the past — on the job, at home, or in a volunteer capacity. Again, take your time. Revisit. Add. Subtract.

2. Then highlight or star the ten or twelve words that describe skills that you have *enjoyed using most*.

3. Now look at the Skill Set headings to determine your *three strongest Skill Sets*. Under which Skill Sets have you checked the most skill words? These indicate which Skill Sets you enjoy using. If your skill words are scattered and do not fall neatly into *three* Skill Sets, go with your first reactions and choose the three Skill Sets that you feel fit best. Or make up new combinations of skill words to form new Skill Sets.

### HAVE FUN WITH THIS !

**Suggestion:** You might have trouble deciding on **three** Skill Sets. This probably is because you don't want to make a mistake and identify the wrong skills. Hey!!! Take your best shot!!! You always can modify later. Nothing is cast in concrete here!

4. When you feel comfortable with your three Skill Sets, write them on your Best-Case Job Summary Sheet.

5. With that accomplished, move on to Skill Stories.

# SKILL SETS

SKILL SET:     **SALES/MARKETING**

| | |
|---|---|
| ✓ Selling | ___Forecasting |
| ___ Presenting | ___Surveying |
| ___ Influencing | ___Promoting |
| ___ Analyzing | ✓ Motivating |
| ___ Meeting Quotas | ✓ Negotiating |

SKILL SET:     **MANAGEMENT/LEADERSHIP**

| | |
|---|---|
| ✓ Budgeting | ___Goal-setting |
| ✓ Communicating | ✓ Planning |
| ___Counseling | ✓ Decision-making |
| ___Delegating | ✓ Listening |
| ___Interviewing | ___Leading |
| ___Directing | ✓ Motivating |
| ___Organizing | ✓ Negotiating |

SKILL SET:     **MANUAL/MECHANICAL**

| | |
|---|---|
| ✓ Assembling | ✓ Moving equipment |
| ___Building | ✓ Operating machinery |
| ✓ Inspecting | ___Repairing equipment |
| ✓ Installing | ✓ Painting/cleaning |
| ✓ Maintaining equipment | ___Fixing/remodeling |

SKILL SET:   **ANALYTICAL/TECHNICAL**

____Compiling data          ____Analyzing data
____Investigating           ____Troubleshooting
_✓_Reasoning                ____Programming
_✓_Evaluating               _✓_Organizing
____Monitoring              ____Conceptualizing
____Systematizing           _✓_Designing


SKILL SET:   **TRAINING/TEACHING**

____Developing programs     ____Listening
____Speaking                ____Writing
____Leading groups          ____Motivating
____Explaining              ____Evaluating
____Creating                ____Assessing needs


SKILL SET:   **COMMUNICATION**

____Interviewing            _✓_Reporting
____Teaching                _✓_Listening
____Counseling              ____Persuading
_✓_Researching             _✓_Presenting
____Editing                 ____Interpreting
_✓_Writing                 _✓_Speaking
_✓_Summarizing             _✓_Grammar/Spelling

SKILL SET: **CREATIVE**
- ✓ Writing
- ✓ Starting new things
- ___ Inventing
- ___ Persuading
- ___ Developing
- ✓ Painting/drawing/sculpting/weaving/etc.
- ___ Innovating
- ✓ Thinking with both left, right brains
- ✓ Organizing
- ✓ Designing
- ___ Interpreting

SKILL SET: **INTERPERSONAL**
- ✓ Advising
- ___ Counseling
- Maintaining:
  - ___ Objectivity
  - ___ Tact and diplomacy
  - ___ Confidentiality
- ✓ Negotiating
- ✓ Consulting
- ✓ Listening
- ✓ Speaking

SKILL SET: **ADMINISTRATIVE/CLERICAL**
- ✓ Organizing
- ___ Prioritizing
- ___ Following instructions
- ___ Juggling many activities
- ___ Working under pressure
- ✓ Planning
- ___ Listening
- ✓ Processing information
- Technical skills:
  - ___ Keyboarding
  - ___ Word processing/adding machining
  - ✓ Keeping records/filing
  - ___ Operating multi-line phone

## SKILL STORIES

Your next task is to write stories. Think of things you have done in the past that were enjoyable, satisfying and fun. *These things are not just work-related*—use hobbies and volunteer activities too. Begin to think about expressing these events or incidents with clarity and succinctness. In order to achieve this clarity and succinctness, use the **What - How - Result** format:

- **What** I did
- **How** I did it
- With what **Result** — WOW !

For example, let's say that you had fun and felt good inside when you organized a company picnic. In order to bring clarity and succinctness to this experience use the What – How – Result — Wow!! format:

**What:**
- This is the first sentence of the story.
- It must answer the question, "What did you do?"

**How:**
- Tells how you accomplished what you claim you did in the first sentence.
- Keep the HOW to between five and eight sentences.
- You should be able to read or tell your story in ninety seconds.

**Result — WOW!**
Tells results of the What and How.
- Quantify if possible:
  - Saved company $50,000.00.
  - Reduced waste by 37%.
  - Earned my company $2 million in a year.

- State unquantifiable results:
  - -After the project was completed, I got a raise.
  - -I felt tremendous satisfaction bringing the project in on time.
  - -My boss said he had rarely seen such competence.
  - -It felt good to help her be a better employee.

**Now . . .**

1. Study the Sample Skill Story Sheets (pp. 92, 93).
   A. Note how each story illustrates the Skill Set stated at the top. Some of the words used in the stories are skill words from those Skills Sets.

   B. Note that each story states specific Results — Wow! It is important to include results for each story.

2. Next, use pages 94-96 (or others) to:
   A. Write one of your Skill Sets at the top of a page.

   B. Using the What - How - Result — Wow! format, write stories, incidents, or events from your past to illustrate how and when you have used the skills.

## WHAT'S THE BIG DEAL ABOUT SKILL STORIES?

Here's the deal. When you are in a job interview, your interviewer wants to know the skills you bring to the position. He or she may say something like, "What we really need is someone who can manage big projects."

("AHA!" you think, "I will tell my Major Move story here.")

"As a matter of fact, I have strong project management skills," you say, "and I have used them in the past to manage a major move successfully. I did that when I was with a doctors' office. May I tell you about it?"

**Yes!**

When you do your homework and prepare skill stories, you prepare yourself for job interviews and resume writing. When you become a skilled storyteller, you become skilled at *articulating your transferable skills both orally and on paper to the people who have the power to hire you.* It is your responsibility to impart your skills well. What - How - Results — Wow! is your method of doing that.

### ONGOING HOMEWORK:

Create a "Skill Stories" section in your Networking Notebook (p. 44). Use the skill story format to develop a bunch, a bundle, a big collection, an imaginary bag full of stories that illustrate your Skill Sets.

Developing skill stories means developing your personal power. Through writing your stories, you will come to understand your accomplishments. You will feel good about yourself. You will understand that your imaginary bag of skill stories is, indeed, portable. You can take into any of your areas of interest.

**DOING THIS HOMEWORK MEANS YOU ARE TAKING YOURSELF SERIOUSLY!**

## SAMPLE SKILL STORY

**Skill Set:** *Management / Leadership*

A story from my past: *I took responsibility for a major move.*

**What I Did:** *I prepared and coordinated a major relocation for a team of doctors.*

**How I Did It:** *The doctors needed more room. That meant either staying where we were and remodeling, or moving to a new suite. I was asked to take charge of this decision-making process. I developed a detailed cost benefit analysis report. Based on my report, the decision was made to move. I worked with the architect to design the new suite. I developed the floor plan which offered a very efficient use of space. I designed all of the custom cabinetry, and did cost comparisons for built-in vs. modular furniture. To stay within budget, I worked very closely with the architect, the building manager and the contractor.*

**Results — Wow!** The results of my efforts were:
- *We received a letter from the building management stating that my efforts had saved approximately $10,000.*
- *I enjoyed working with the details of the year-long project.*
- *I loved developing an idea and being involved with all the steps in seeing it come together.*

## SAMPLE SKILL STORY

**Skill Set:** *Training / Teaching*

A story from my past: *I recruited canvassers to get donations.*

**What I Did:** *In one year I greatly increased donations to the American Cancer Society.*

**How I Did It:** *Door-to-door solicitation is not a task many find enjoyable, so I had to be creative in my recruiting. I began by educating groups of women about their risk of breast cancer and the need for self-examination and having mammograms. I then made them aware of their responsibility to inform other women and took the names of volunteers who were willing to carry the message to 10 houses and at the same time accept contributions. Soon I had other women who were recruiting. I finally had 47 women going door-to-door to educate others and collect money.*

**Results — Wow!** *The results of my efforts were that:*
- *I increased my area's income by 400%.*
- *I enjoyed educating the women.*
- *I received an award for outstanding service from the American Cancer Society.*

## SKILL STORY

Skill Set: _____

A story from my past:

### What I Did:

### How I Did It:

### RESULTS — Wow!

## SKILL STORY

Skill Set: _____

A story from my past:

**What I Did:**

**How I Did It:**

**Results — Wow!**

## SKILL STORY

Skill Set: _____

A story from my past:

**What I Did:**

**How I Did It:**

**Results — Wow!**

## THE REST OF THE PICTURE

The following pages contain other exercises that will help you identify the elements of your "best-case" job.

Be thoughtful as you are doing them, and then compile your conclusions on your Best-Case Job Summary Sheet. When this is completed, you will have something to measure job opportunities against.

Ask yourself, "Does this job contain elements of my Best-Case job?"

If not, better say, "No thanks."

If so, better say, "Yes!"

You will stimulate your mind and memory as you consider these areas to determine your Best-Case work:

- Work Values
- People
- Money
- Location
- Working Conditions
- Best-Case Job Summary Sheet

## WORK VALUES

Go through the following list of work values and check the ten that you feel you must have on the job in order to be happy and productive. You function best in an environment that offers you:

- ☑ Independence
- ___ Little structure
- ☑ Open communication
- ___ Lots of structure
- ___ Advancement
- ___ The ability to make decisions
- ___ Great responsibility
- ___ Power and authority
- ☑ The sharing of ideas
- ___ Little responsibility
- ___ A fast work pace
- ___ Moderate structure
- ___ Physical challenge
- ___ A diverse mix of co-workers
- ___ A team approach to gender/ethnic/racial problem-solving
- ☑ Learning opportunities
- ☑ Humor in the workplace
- ___ Time freedom
- ___ Moral/spiritual fulfillment
- ☑ Flexibility
- ___ Moderate responsibility
- ___ Creativity
- ___ Security
- ___ Stimulating co-workers

Add your own: _____

After you have checked your top ten, hone the list to the five work values that you **absolutely can not live without**. Write them here.

These are your five strongest work values:

1. _____

2. _____

3. _____

4. _____

5. _____

## PEOPLE

There are people *and* there are people... all kinds with all sorts of positive and negative characteristics. If you could surround yourself with ideal people in an ideal work environment, check the ten characteristics that those people would exhibit. My ideal people are:

- ✓ Good communicators
- ___ Easy-going
- ✓ Fair-minded
- ✓ Goal-oriented
- ___ Able to say they made a mistake... (humble)
- ___ Optimistic
- ___ Of high integrity
- ___ Direct (I know where I stand)
- ___ Good delegators
- ___ Visionary
- ___ Competitive
- ___ Self-possessed (is him/herself consistently)

- ___ Professional
- ✓ Trusting
- ___ Competent
- ___ Risk-takers
- ✓ Appreciative of humor
- ___ Democratic
- ✓ Honest
- ✓ Considerate of my personal wants/needs
- ___ Good listeners
- ___ Accepting of all kinds of people

After you have checked your top ten, hone the list to the five characteristics you *absolutely can not live without*.

These are your five most important people characteristics:

1. _____

2. _____

3. _____

4. _____

5. _____

# MONEY

It is helpful to take a realistic look at the money you want to make. To do this, start with what you are making now. Do some budgeting to arrive at SURVIVAL, BASIC NEEDS + and IDEAL.

## Present

Including all sources of income, state your current annual earnings:

$ _____

## Survival

If you found a smashing job — one that you would love to show up to each day, what minimum salary would you accept in order to take the job, assuming more money would be forth-coming in the next six months or so?

$ _____

## Basic Needs +

Considering your present needs, what salary would cause you to feel comfortable: all bills paid, including savings and things like college funds plus some left for fun/recreation?

$ _____

## Ideal

Looking at the ideal, how much would you like to make? This means thinking about a new house, boat, travel, etc., being able to pay for it all, including savings, college funds plus fun/recreation?

$ _____

## Benefits

Retirement funds, life and disability insurance, health insurance, etc. often are as important—or more so —than dollars earned. Think through your requirements and other resources in these areas.

Then list benefits that you feel you absolutely need:

Health

Dental

vision

## LOCATION

Employment opportunities abound in many different geographical locations. Ask yourself what your geographical preferences are.

Check one: ——— I am a "city kid." I want to live in a city of:

—— Small (3-500,000 pop.)
—— Mid-size (5-700,000 pop.)
—— Large (700, 000+ pop.)

——— I prefer the suburbs of a:

—— Mid-size city
—— Large city

——— I prefer rural living with one-hour access to a city.

List other amenities you must have in or near your location:

___ Stage plays
___ Classical music
___ Opera
___ Good restaurants
___ Professional sports teams
___ Mountains
___ Beach/oceans
___ Others: Add your own preferences:

Climate: Describe the climate you would like to live in:

_____

_____

_____

Write your Location preferences here:

Size of city  _____

Three amenities  _____ , _____ and

_____

Climate  _____

# WORKING CONDITIONS

You work best in surroundings that are comfortable for you, doing things that you like to do. Give some thought to your ideal working conditions.

I like a:    \_\_\_\_ small company (2 - 20 people)

\_\_\_\_ medium company ( 21 - 100 people)

\_\_\_\_ larger company (101 - 800 people)

\_\_\_\_ corporate set-up (801 - thousands)

I like to dress:    \_\_\_\_ professionally every day:
*(Check one)*        (suits, dresses)

\_\_\_\_ casually:

(slacks, skirts, sweaters)

\_\_\_\_ a little of both:

(flexible dress code)

I am most comfortable when:
*(check one)*  \_\_\_\_ managing/leading/supervising

\_\_\_\_ taking direction from others

\_\_\_\_ directing my own work load

I enjoy:    \_\_\_\_ showing up to a variety of tasks
*(check two)*       each day

\_\_\_\_ showing up to a routine

\_\_\_\_ a quiet, stable work atmosphere

\_\_\_\_ a volatile, changing work atmosphere

Other:    List any other working conditions that you know are important to your happiness and productivity:

_____

_____

_____

_____

Write your five most important working conditions here:

1. _____

2. _____

3. _____

4. _____

5. _____

## YOUR BEST-CASE JOB

1. Now, take the information from the bottom of each exercise you have just completed and transfer it to the appropriate place on your Best-Case Job Summary Sheet. The information on your Best-Case Job Summary Sheet provides you with a personal filtering mechanism for deciding which job(s) are best for you.

2. After each information interview, write answers to **Filtering Questions** (p. 59) in your Networking Notebook. This is how you filter information through your Best-Case Job Summary Sheet and make solid decisions about what you want. In other words, ask yourself after each Researching interview, "What did I learn that fits my best-case job? What doesn't fit? Where do I go from here?"

# MY BEST-CASE JOB SUMMARY SHEET

My reality: I am happiest and most productive at work connecting with these **Interests**:

1. _____
2. _____
3. _____

. . . using these **Skill Sets**:

1. _____
2. _____
3. _____

. . . and these **Work Values:**

1. _____
2. _____
3. _____
4. _____
5. _____

. . . in an environment that contains these kinds of
   **People**

1. _____
2. _____

People: (cont.)

3. _____

4. _____

5. _____
   . . . making this kind of **Money**:

   Survival    _____

   Basic       _____

   Ideal       _____

   . . . in this **Location**:  Size: _____

Amenities:  _____ , _____ and

            _____

Climate:    _____

   . . . with these **Working Conditions**:

   1. _____

   2. _____

   3. _____

   4. _____

   5. _____

MAKE A COPY OF THIS INFORMATION FOR YOUR
NETWORKING NOTEBOOK.

## FOCUS SHEET

### Focus: THREE INTERESTS

Your job search should be enjoyable. It **will** be enjoyable if you take your interests seriously. Select three interests that would be fun for you to explore. They can be industries, companies or job titles. Write them here:

1. _____

2. _____

3. _____

This is your focus, your starting point. You can add other interest areas as you progress with your job search, but this is where you begin!

### Focus: FIVE PEOPLE

You begin researching your areas of interest by talking to people to find out how your skills and values fit with their industries, companies or job titles. Write the names of five people with whom you will begin your research:

1. _____

2. _____

3. _____

4. _____

5. _____

If you need help identifying five people with whom to begin your job search, ask people you already know to help you. ***Your most valuable resource in your job search is other people ... open your mouth and ask for help.***

### Focus: NETWORKING NOTEBOOK

If you are not organized in your job search you will lose credibility. Set up your networking notebook now!

### Focus: BUSINESS (CONFETTI) CARDS

Buy business cards. Name, address and phone only. You cannot do a professional and credible job search without them!

### Focus: PICK UP THE PHONE

This is where the rubber meets the road. Call those five people, go see them, then send a "Thank You." Keep in touch. Find out what's out there for you!

# APPENDICES

**A.** PERSPECTIVES: STAYING ON TRACK

**B.** NETWORKING NOTEBOOK SAMPLES

# PERSPECTIVES: STAYING ON TRACK

- If you are constantly thinking about getting to the end of your job search, you will not enjoy the process on a daily basis. You must concentrate on what you are doing right now, and what you will do next. That's how you will get to the end.

- If you are working full time and want to begin a job search, make a commitment to yourself to do one Researching interview each week. People will meet with you before work, after work, during lunch and on Saturdays or Sundays. If you can handle two or three Researching interviews per week, do them! The point is to get going with the process.

- Sometimes you can't get there from here. You might know what you want to do, but you can't do it now. Don't throw your dream away. Begin thinking in life-planning terms. What will you do in the meantime? What kind of work can you do that is related to the long term goal?

- Do not let your fear keep you from beginning the process. The truth is you do not know how to do Researching perfectly. The truth is you are uneasy about calling people. The truth is you probably don't want to do any of this, because it looks big and ugly and you feel inadequate to the task. Don't forget that you are learning new skills. You cannot expect perfection without practice. Your confidence will grow with each call you make.

- Remember that your job search takes as long as it takes. Don't say things like, "Well, I will have my new job in three months." This artificial deadline will cause nothing but anxiety. As the time draws near and there are no solid opportunities on the horizon, you will feel awful.

- *Never, ever take a resume on an information interview ! ! !*

- Go with what feels good and right to you. Do not deny your interests in favor of logic or what you think you "should" be doing.

- Create your own good luck by following the Prime Rule of the job search: *Open your mouth and talk to people!!*

- Review the Ten Truths periodically to keep in touch with the reality of the job search/career exploration process.

- You know you're doing it right when you feel positive and energized and you're smiling a lot.

# NETWORKING NOTEBOOK SAMPLES

- TARGET THE CALL SHEET
- SAMPLE NOTEBOOK PAGE
- SKILL STORY SHEET

## TARGET THE CALL SAMPLE

| Name of the person I'm going to call. | Name of the person who referred me. | AGENDA: What do I want from this person? |
|---|---|---|
| *Mike Green*<br><br>*555-7712* | *Shirley Quinn* | Say: *I am in a Career Exploration, and I'm interested in knowing more about the food industry. Shirley Quinn suggested I call because you have been in the industry for some time. I would like to talk with you for about 20 minutes on Tuesday or Thursday to learn more about the industry and whether or not it might match with my career interests.* |

• SET UP TARGET THE CALL SHEETS IN YOUR NETWORKING NOTEBOOK •

# NETWORKING NOTEBOOK: SAMPLE PAGE

*Green, Mike*
   *ABC Foods*
   *555-7712*

*Referral: Shirley Quinn*
*Called 10/18*
*Appt: 10-21 — Info Interview 10:30*

*Thank You: 10-23*

*Referrals:    Bill Jones*
              *Sally Peters*

*NOTES:*

```
┌─────────────────────────────────────┐
│            ABC Foods                 │
│                                      │
│           Mike Green                 │
│            Marketing                 │
│                                      │
│  1119 7th St.  Portland, OR  97888   │
│            (503) 555-7712            │
└─────────────────────────────────────┘
```

• DON'T NEGLECT YOUR FILTERING QUESTIONS •

**SKILL STORY SHEET:**

**SKILL SET:**_____

A story from my past:

**What I Did:**

**How I Did It:**

**Results — Wow!**

**REMEMBER: Develop a bundle, bunch, *Big Collection* of Skill Stories for use in interviewing and on resumes!**

• PUT A SKILL STORIES SECTION IN YOUR
NETWORKING NOTEBOOK •

**Pam Gross**, founder of CareerMakers, used her teaching and program development skills to grow CareerMakers into a dynamic life planning and job search program which has served more than 2,000 people since 1983. She also wrote a self-directed career management program for corporate use, and designs corporate training programs based on material in this book.

Before becoming a Northwesterner, Pam had a 15-year public school teaching career in Michigan, Ohio, Kentucky, Indiana, and California. Throughout her life she has combined work with extensive church and community involvement. For her work at CareerMakers, she was recognized by *The Oregonian* newspaper as an outstanding "Woman of the '90's " managing a "Business of the '90's." Pam is a powerful speaker who expresses job search and career issues with a rare combination of passion and practicality. She is a graduate of Wayne State University.

Since 1984 **Peter Paskill** has provided career counseling to more than 2,000 individual clients, and presented workshops and seminars to thousands more. As an active member of both Pacific Northwest Personnel Manager's Association and Society for Human Resources Management, Peter is an incisive consultant to businesses. He frequently serves on panels and makes speeches about job search issues.

Reared and educated in the Northwest, Peter had a successful business career both in management and personnel before joining CareerMakers. As a survivor of his own unemployment crisis, Peter shares his experiences with individuals and with businesses in a pragmatic "street-smart" manner. He is a University of Oregon graduate.